DR BENJA [...] Daniels is the pseudonym of a doctor currently working for the NHS. He can be reached at drbenjamindaniels@hotmail.co.uk and @drbendaniels on twitter.

Also by Dr Benjamin Daniels

Confessions of a GP

DR BENJAMIN DANIELS

Further Confessions of a GP

THE FRIDAY PROJECT

The Friday Project
An imprint of HarperCollins*Publishers*
77–85 Fulham Palace Road
Hammersmith
London W6 8JB

www.harpercollins.co.uk

This edition published by The Friday Project 2014

1

First published in Great Britain by The Friday Project as an ebook in 2013

Benjamin Daniels asserts the moral right to be identified
as the author of this work
A catalogue record for this book is available from the British Library

ISBN 978-0-00-752495-2

Printed and bound in Great Britain by Clays Ltd, St Ives plc

MIX
Paper from
responsible sources
FSC www.fsc.org   FSC™ C007454

Disclaimer

The events described in this book are based on my experiences as a GP. For obvious reasons of privacy and confidentiality I have made certain changes, altered identifying features and fictionalised some aspects. Nonetheless, it remains an honest reflection of life as a doctor in Britain today. This is what it's like. These things really happen!

This book is dedicated to my family and to coffee. If it wasn't for my family the book would have been finished a year earlier. If it wasn't for coffee it wouldn't have been finished at all.

Introduction

'Oh, and just one more thing, Doc, before I go. I'm reading this book …' With that my patient pulled out a copy of *Confessions of a GP* from his bag. 'Have you read it?'

'No,' I lied, then added bravely, 'Is it any good?'

'It's all right, I suppose. Could definitely be a lot funnier and the author comes across as a bit of a self-righteous prat at times. I'll lend it to you once I've finished it, if you like?'

'Nah, you're all right.'

I wrote *Confessions of a GP* a few years ago, all about my experiences as a newly qualified GP. Partly due to the witty anecdotes and insightful social commentary, but mostly due to the extremely low pricing of the ebook version, it sold surprisingly well, and so I decided to write this sequel. I penned the first book while working as a nomadic locum doctor. I have now settled as a partner in an inner city practice and I also work a regular shift each week in our local A&E department.

These are my further confessions.

First day

'You're not Dr Bailey.'

'No, Dr Bailey's wife had a stroke yesterday and he is taking some time off to help care for her.'

'But who's going to look after me?'

'Well, I'm going to be looking after Dr Bailey's patients while he's away.'

'You're no good,' Mrs Patrick huffed, looking me up and down. 'You don't even know me. I always see Dr Bailey. When's he coming back?'

'I don't know. His wife is really quite poorly.'

Mrs Patrick tutted loudly and I was left wondering if she was more upset with me for not being Dr Bailey, or Dr Bailey's wife for selfishly having a stroke.

'Might I be able to help at all? What's brought you into the doctor's surgery today?'

By this stage I was rather hoping that her obvious lack of faith in my abilities would lead to a short and easy consultation, but unfortunately Mrs Patrick sat glued to the seat for another 30 minutes. An endless array of intolerable sufferings were described in gruesome detail, but before allowing me to offer any possible solutions,

3

she would curtly remind me that I couldn't possibly help and how dreadful it was that Dr Bailey had left her in the lurch like this.

Most of the morning's patients offered a little more sympathy for Dr Bailey's predicament, but none seemed to consider me a worthy understudy. By the time I drove off on my first visit of my new job, I was feeling thoroughly demoralised.

My visit took me to a small house set back from the main road. An elderly gentleman with a warm face greeted me at the door with such an affectionate welcome that I was encouraged to believe that I might finally have met a patient who viewed me to be of some worth. As I reached out for a formal handshake, he clutched my hand in both of his and took an eternity to let go.

'We so appreciate you coming out to see us what with it being your first day, Dr Daniels. My wife is upstairs. Are you going to bring her down?'

'Erm, what do you mean bring her down?'

'She can't really manage the stairs these days, so Dr Bailey always carries her down to the lounge.'

My face must have given away my surprise and the kind old gent apologetically attempted to take back his request. 'Well if you're not able to manage her, Dr Daniels, I'm sure …'

'No no,' I interrupted. 'I'm sure I'll manage just fine.' I was determined to match the feats of the mighty Dr Bailey on at least one occasion today.

Mrs Alexander didn't weigh a great deal, but it wasn't easy hoisting her up into a fireman's hold and then navigating the narrow winding staircase. I'm fairly sure it wasn't a technique advised on the 'Lifting and Handling' course I was forced to go on before I was allowed to qualify as a doctor. As I finally lowered Mrs Alexander on to the sofa, I tried not to look too exhausted by the whole ordeal.

'Right, what can I do for you then Mrs Alexander?'

'I'm all bunged up again, Doctor. I haven't opened my bowels for two weeks.'

As I started to list the various laxatives and suppositories I could prescribe, Mr Alexander politely interrupted me.

'None of those work for my wife, Dr Daniels. That's why Dr Bailey has to clear it out himself.'

'Excuse me?'

'We put a towel down on the carpet here and Elsie lies down on it. We've got some spare gloves and Vaseline in the cupboard and Dr Bailey just puts his finger in and clears all the hard stuff out. He says it's the only way once it gets to this stage.'

Before I could think of any way to object, Mr Alexander had neatly laid out the towel and Mrs Alexander was hitching up her nightie.

'I think these gloves will fit,' he said as he offered me a pair of medium-sized marigolds.

I had smugly managed to avoid ever having to do a manual evacuation up until now. I can vividly recall the occasion when one of the consultant surgeons made all the medical students in his team stand in a line with our hands held out in front of us. He walked up and down inspecting our outstretched fingers, searching for the slimmest and daintiest of digits to clear out the particularly tightly packed rectum that he had waiting to be evacuated of its hardened contents. I can still recall the relief I felt as I looked down at my short podgy fingers and then compared them to the delicate little hands of the Japanese girl standing to my left. I could almost smell her terror growing as she realised that the consultant was studying her beautiful slim fingers with some excitement. As he led her away to meet her fate, I looked down at my ugly, portly fingers and offered them an instant and unconditional pardon for their fat clumsiness and for all the tasks of dexterity for which they had previously failed me.

My luck had clearly run out though, today. There was no elegant-fingered Japanese medical student to save me this time, so I donned the gloves, took a deep breath and got stuck in. The urge to gag was almost overwhelming as I methodically used my index finger to pick out the rock-hard lumps that were blocking Mrs Alexander's rectum. As I probed my finger further and further into the depths of her lower bowel, I finally managed to break through that last solid stubborn layer of rigid faeces. There was an ominous rumbling, an almighty stench and then the satisfying passage of soft stool leaking past my finger. I could see Mrs Alexander's tight, distended abdomen deflating before my eyes.

It was an oddly satisfying experience and I gave myself a metaphorical pat on the back for having finally matched up to the lofty achievements of the wonderful Dr Bailey. I made a swift exit, and as Mr Alexander got on with cleaning up the results of my handiwork, I hurried back to the relative sanctity of the surgery.

As I walked through the door, the receptionist was holding the phone and covering the mouthpiece with her hand.

'It's Mr Alexander on the phone. He's not very happy with you,' she whispered.

'Bloody hell! What more do these people want from me?'

'Apparently Mrs Alexander is stuck in the lounge because you carried her downstairs but forgot to take her back up to her bedroom again before you left. You'll have to pop back in on your way home tonight. They keep asking me when Dr Bailey is coming back ...'

That was over three years ago now. Despite my disastrous first day, when Dr Bailey decided he wasn't going to return, the surgery offered to keep me on as his permanent replacement. Initially, I was reluctant to give up my nomadic locum lifestyle, but with advancing years, I craved some stability and decided to stay. I soon found this quirky little GP surgery and its patients growing on me, and I've been here ever since.

Sarah

When Sarah walked in she looked familiar, but I couldn't work out why. It was only my first week at the new surgery, so she hadn't been to see me previously as a patient. I was going to suggest that we might somehow know each other, but before I had the chance, she launched into a long monologue relating her constipation and dodgy bowel symptoms in some detail. Suddenly, I remembered where we had met before. She was the sister of a girl that my friend Pete had gone out with about 15 years ago. We had met a few times, and I can clearly recall that I once went to a party at her house and made a very drunken and unsuccessful attempt to chat her up. After being very unsubtly rebuffed, I'd decided to drown my sorrows by drinking some more and ended up vomiting into her empty bathtub. As if that wasn't bad enough, for some reason I then concluded that despite the bath vomit I was still in with a good shot with Sarah after all, and made another doomed attempt to chat her up. A good memory is a must for a career in medicine, but at times like this I really wish my powers of recollection weren't quite so efficient.

With Sarah not appearing to remember me, it was tempting to ignore our previous acquaintance and continue the consultation in the normal way. However, I couldn't believe that she wouldn't remember me at some point and so I really needed to find an appropriate moment to mention that I wasn't the anonymous doctor she thought I was. I was just considering how best to broach the subject when my hand was forced

'Doctor, do you think you should have a look at them?'

'Sorry?' I had been miles away and completely missed the last couple of things Sarah had been telling me.

'My piles, Doctor. I think you might need to take a look.'

Now was the time, I really needed to come clean.

'Sarah, I could have a look at your piles, but I think you need to know that we have in fact met before.'

Sarah looked at me puzzled. 'But I thought you were the new doctor?'

'Yes, I am, but I think we actually met some years ago. You've a sister called Jeanette and she was going out with my friend Pete for a bit.'

'Yeah, that's right,' she said. Her face lit up, clearly remembering Pete, but then she frowned as she looked me up and down, still having no clue at all as to where I fitted in.

This was getting really painful. I waited a bit, hoping that Sarah would remember me without further prompting, but unable to bear the awkwardness any longer I started to fill in the gaps.

'I used to live with Pete and we met a few times …'

Suddenly, Sarah threw her hand over her mouth as the penny finally dropped.

'Oh my god. You're that bloke who tried to … and then you vomited in my … and then you tried again to …'

By this point Sarah was clearly remembering me with some horror. If she was trying to conceal her overwhelming feeling of disgust, she was doing an extremely poor job.

'And they let you become a doctor?' she added finally, with a combination of surprise and dismay.

'Er, yeah ... I mean, well, that was a long time ago, wasn't it?'

Thankfully, drunken vomiting in inappropriate places and failed attempts at seduction are not considered exclusion criteria for graduating from medical school. If they were I think there would be a massive world shortage of doctors and absolutely no orthopaedic surgeons whatsoever.

When I was simply the anonymous new doctor, Sarah had been only too happy to describe to me her bowel movements in bewildering detail and had no qualms about presenting to me the haemorrhoids protruding from her backside. Now that I had been exposed as the drunken idiot who once tried to chat her up after vomiting in her bathtub, she seemed less enamoured with the idea.

'Maybe it would be better if I waited for Dr Bailey to come back. I mean, I've known him for years. You know, as like a doctor rather than someone who ... well, you know.'

By this point, I already knew that Dr Bailey wasn't coming back, but before I had the chance to explain that, Sarah was out the door. In fact, her getaway was almost as quick as the one she'd made 15 years ago when we last met.

Crackhead Kenny I

It was 4 a.m. and I had just given myself a little hit of coffee and chocolate in an attempt to help drag myself through those last few painful hours of an A&E night shift. The caffeine was giving me palpitations and an odd buzzing sensation, but not successfully eradicating the overwhelming hazy blur of exhaustion. It had only been an hour since I had necked two cans of Red Bull, but I just needed one more coffee to help me muster the energy to see my next patient.

Despite having one wrist handcuffed to a prison officer and the other hand chained to the metal frame of the trolley, Kenny was, metaphorically, bouncing off the ceiling. The prison officer's grey and expressionless face was in stark contrast to his prisoner's, whose beaming grin and intense shining eyes were almost mesmerising. It was apparent that the drugs market within our local prison could provide stimulants considerably stronger than my vending-machine coffee and out-of-date Twix bar.

Kenny reached out his cuffed hand, but I paused. There is something about someone being handcuffed that makes me automatically think he must be horrendously dangerous. If I took his hand would he somehow be able to slip out of his cuffs and take me hostage?

Being taken hostage by a drug-crazed prisoner is a scenario I would handle particularly badly. Looking Kenny up and down, I realised that my sleep deprivation was making me paranoid. Kenny really didn't look very dangerous. He was scruffy and scrawny, but his missing teeth didn't inhibit his childlike smile. I reached out my hand and he gave me a warm and enthusiastic handshake.

'I'm Kenny, but all my friends call me Crackhead Kenny.'

'I'm Dr Ben, but all my friends call me Big Nose Benny.'

I instantly regretted the informality of my response, but I often find myself slightly less reserved during the early hours of the morning. It's as if patient-doctor etiquette has a vaguely different set of rules at night. Either that or I simply become increasingly inappropriate the more sleep deprived I become.

'I reckon my nickname trumps yours,' Kenny declared triumphantly.

'I suppose, but you'll have to change yours when you stop taking crack. I'll always have a big nose.'

'True,' he nodded. 'But I reckon I'll always be Crackhead Kenny,' he added ruefully

I wanted to ask Kenny why he was in prison, but it was none of my business really, so instead I stuck with the more conventional question of why he was in hospital.

'Well, I fell over and these clowns are covering their arses, so they wanted me in here for a check over.'

I looked over to the prison officer for some sort of response but his face remained expressionless. I wondered exactly what it would take to prise any sort of emotion out of him.

I started scanning Kenny's medical record and noticed with some surprise his date of birth.

'We've got exactly the same birthday.'

Kenny looked at me oddly.

14

'We were both born on 6 March 1977.'

'We're time twins!' Kenny shouted enthusiastically.

'Yes, we are,' I replied smiling, unable not to be caught up in Kenny's infectious drug-induced gusto.

'I tell you another thing we've got in common, Dr Ben. As a boy I always dreamed of being a doctor. I wanted to do something good with my life. I really wanted to help people and make them better. I also liked the idea of driving a nice car and flirting with lots of sexy nurses.' He gave me a wink. 'Although I think I might have left it a little late now,' he added ruefully.

'It's never too late to flirt with the nurses, Kenny, but I'd give our charge nurse Barry a wide birth. He's a grumpy old bugger.'

'Yeah, I spotted him on my way in. Perhaps a career in medicine isn't for me after all.'

Maybe it was just too much emotion caused by lack of sleep, but I couldn't help but feel a connection with Kenny. Sharing a date of birth is fairly insignificant really, in the big scheme of things, but at four in the morning during our peculiar substance-enhanced encounter, it seemed to hold some meaning.

I imagined us both as small babies, beginning our lives on that same day. We would have started off similarly enough as two equally innocent infant boys, new and full of potential. Our first steps and first words would have coincided and at some point during our childhoods we both decided that we wanted to be doctors. What had ebbed away at Kenny's potential while mine was being steadfastly encouraged?

After giving Kenny a quick check over, I wandered out to the nurses' station where Barry the charge nurse was slumped in his chair looking unshakably miserable. I told him about the connection I'd made with my time twin and reflected on why and how our lives had taken such different paths.

'He's just a smack head who happens to share your birthday. Stop being a sentimental twat and get some work done. Most importantly, get him discharged before he comes down off whatever he's taken and starts kicking off.'

As I finished writing up his notes, the prison officer walked Kenny out of the department to his waiting van. 'My carriage awaits!' he exclaimed giving me a regal wave with his non-cuffed hand. 'See ya later, Big Nose Benny.'

'Nice meeting you, Crackhead Kenny.'

Maggie I

'It's my leg, Doctor. It doesn't really do what I want it to do. It's as if it's not really part of me any more.' Maggie tried to crack a smile but I could see she was really scared.

'Right, let's have a look then.'

Maggie was quite right. Her left leg wasn't doing what it was supposed to be doing. She could sort of move it, but her coordination was shot and she had resorted to walking with a stick.

'I'm walking like an old lady, but I'm only 56. It just came on over the weekend and it's getting worse.'

Maggie was clearly looking for some reassurance, but the truth was that I was worried too.

'We need to get this looked into,' I said, stating the obvious.

I'd met Maggie a few times, but usually only when she was accompanying her husband for his blood pressure appointments.

'Any medical problems in the past?' I asked as I scanned through her notes.

'No, I'm fit as a flea. Well, I had breast cancer in 2003, but that's long gone. It can't be anything to do with that.'

I looked up from my computer screen and she held my gaze. I was trying to find words that might be both reassuring and honest, but before I could even open my mouth, Maggie was crying.

'The breast cancer's all gone,' she blubbed, trying to convince herself more than convince me. 'They discharged me from the clinic five years ago.'

'It may well be nothing to do with the breast cancer, but let's just get some tests done.'

Maggie clearly needed to see a specialist and have a scan. She didn't really need to be admitted to hospital that morning, but then it wasn't appropriate to make her wait two weeks for an outpatient appointment either. When stuck with this sort of quandary, I generally default to the 'What would I want if it was me?' option. This turned the decision into a bit of a no-brainer and I phoned the medical consultant on call who agreed that she should go straight up to the hospital.

Sometimes it's really satisfying to get a diagnosis right, but I took no pleasure in having my suspicions confirmed this time. Maggie's leg symptoms were due to her breast cancer returning. It had already spread extensively and it was lesions in the brain that were causing her leg symptoms. After being told the result of the scan she was discharged with some steroids.

Maggie had still been in a state of shock when they'd given her the diagnosis in hospital, so she made an appointment with me to go over a few things. First of all she wanted to know how the cancer had lain dormant for all those years before coming back. I would like to have been able to answer that question, but the truth was I just didn't know. It wasn't something she'd done wrong; it was just one of those awful facts about cancer. Sometimes we think we have beaten it, yet somehow this horrible disease has a dirty habit of reappearing. Maggie hadn't even noticed a breast lump, but by the time she had her scan there were cancerous lesions in her liver, bones and brain. The cancer specialist offered her some chemotherapy that might temporarily shrink the tumours, but he made it very clear that he could offer her no cure.

'What now?' was her next question.

Again, this was a hard one to answer. 'We'll get the palliative care nurses involved and will always make sure that you're never in pain or distress with the symptoms. You might remain stable and fairly well for some time ...'

'But basically I'm going to die.'

I thought about trying to counter that remark with something upbeat and positive, but in reality Maggie was right. She was going to die and I couldn't say anything that would change that fact. I stayed quiet, handed her a tissue and put my hand on her hand. We sat in silence for a few moments while she sobbed. After she left, I made myself a quick cup of tea, splashed some cold water on my face and pulled myself together enough to see my next patient.

Brian and Deidre

Every couple of months or so the surgery shuts for an afternoon and we have some sort of educational session. It's an attempt to keep us up to date and make us better doctors. The most recent education afternoon was on the topic of sexual health. A lady with a colourful silk scarf and ethnic sandals was talking to us about the importance of sexual identity.

'How often do you see your patients as sexual beings?' she asked. 'How often do you consider how the medications you prescribe might affect the sexuality of your patients?' I had to admit that the answer to both of these questions was 'never'. I knew that some medications could affect libido and erections, but I tended to avoid discussing it with patients if I could. This was all going to change from now on, though, I decided. The sex therapist lady was right. There was no point lowering a patient's blood pressure if I was going to ruin his relationship because my drugs were inhibiting his erections.

The first chance to demonstrate my newfound sensitivity came the very next day. Brian had come in for a review of his blood pressure medication. I know it's wrong to pigeonhole, but I always felt like Brian looked like the perfect stereotype of a bus driver:

mid-50s, with mutton-chop sideburns and an ever-expanding beer belly. His faded white shirt always had large yellow sweat patches in his armpits and was open at the neck to reveal a big gold chain that matched his sovereign rings. Brian was accompanied by his wife Deidre, and although they always came to see me together, I had the impression that their relationship was often strained. With my new approach, perhaps I could help?

'Brian, some men find that beta-blocker medication like the one you're taking for your blood pressure can affect their ability to have erections. Do you ever find this to be a problem?'

'Well, funny you should say that, Doctor. Me and the wife here have been struggling to manage in the bedroom department for some time. When we're alone together I just can't seem to get the little fella to stand to attention these days.'

Wow, I think to myself. What a breakthrough. The nice sex therapist lady was right. We do need to talk more about sex with our patients. Perhaps I can make a real difference to Brian and Deidre's relationship. Perhaps the sexual frustration is the reason why they're always bickering.

'Mind you, I do still get erections though, Doctor,' Brian said, interrupting my thought process.

'This young lass got on the bus last Tuesday. It was a right warm day if you remember and, cor blimey Dr Daniels, you should have seen her! Gorgeous she was. Legs this long and a little top that didn't leave much to the imagination if you catch my drift …'

Brian went on to explain in some detail each item of his young passenger's clothing, and the relative part of her anatomy that was exposed as a result. 'Rock solid I was, Doctor. Could barely keep the bus on the road! I could see her in my rear-view mirror and I had wood from the stop outside Boots on the high road all the way to the leisure centre past South Street. That's five stops, and I got caught at the lights just before the bridge. I really don't think it's the blood pressure tablets that are the problem, Doctor. I think it might be Deidre. She's not the woman she was. Just doesn't really do it for me any more.'

Deidre had been sitting quietly up until now, but I could sense her rising fury. 'Don't you worry, Dr Daniels, erection or no erection, Brian doesn't do a great deal for me either these days. In fact, he never really did. Even when we were young I always had a lot more fun on my own, if you know what I mean.'

Brian and Deidre went on to describe each other's inadequacies in the bedroom department in some detail. To make things even more awkward, they didn't speak directly to each other but instead spoke to me as if the other wasn't present. I sank as deeply as I possibly could into my chair and cursed myself for turning what could have been a nice simple consultation into something so toe-curlingly awkward that I wished the ground would swallow me up. I tried to think of some useful interjections, but I was well out of my depth with this one, so instead I sat excruciatingly silent until Brian and Deidre decided that I had heard enough and left.

My brief attempt at viewing my patients as 'sexual beings' was well and truly over.

Maggie II

Maggie had come back to see me after seeing the cancer specialist again.

'He was very nice, but he soon discharged me when I decided that I wasn't going to have any chemotherapy.'

'How are you coping?'

'Everyone keeps telling me how brave I am. They tell me I'm a fighter and that I'm strong. I'm fucking dying and they just talk to me about staying positive. The problem is, Dr Daniels, I'm not that brave or strong or positive. Right now I'm scared. In fact, I'm thoroughly terrified. It's as if I'm not allowed to admit it to anyone because I have to be so godforsaking brave the whole bloody time.'

'It's okay. You're allowed to be scared.'

'How about fucking terrified?'

'Yup, that too.'

'I'm all right when people are around or when I'm busy, but when everyone else is out and I'm alone in the house, I can't stop myself from wondering about the end. How will it be? Will I be in pain? Will it be next week or still months away? Will I stop breathing first or will it be my heart that stops? Will I already be in a coma or will I feel myself dying? I need to have some power over this. Sometimes I wish I could piss off to Switzerland and end it all now. I just want to wrestle back control over this whole sodding thing.'

Regardless of the person with the cancer, the same clichés seem to recur time and time again. One of which is sufferers of the disease being universally thought of as 'brave'. The public image is of 'brave' cancer sufferers heroically running marathons while defiantly sporting their chemotherapy-induced baldness. It's as if the brave label arrives the moment you are diagnosed with cancer and you're not allowed to be anything else. Reality TV personality Jade Goody morphed from being a national hate figure to being some sort of serene martyr the moment she was given her cancer diagnosis. In fact, such was the furore when she died that some people were calling for cervical cancer to be renamed 'Jade Goody disease'. I thought I was going to have to start telling people that their smear revealed some abnormal Jade Goody cells on their cervix or that the Goody had spread to their liver. Jesus, as if breaking bad news isn't hard enough already!

It wasn't that Maggie was any less brave than anyone else. She was having a thoroughly normal reaction to the knowledge that she was going to die. We hadn't really known each other well before her diagnosis, but she seemed to have acquired an immense trust in me since I spotted that she had cancer. To be fair, it wasn't some sort of clever diagnosis worthy of *House*, but she clearly appreciated me sending her straight into hospital that first afternoon. There was no cure, but we were going to do everything we could to 'keep her comfortable'. There's another classic cancer cliché that Maggie hates.

Communication skills

Once a year our surgery sends out hundreds of anonymous patient satisfaction questionnaires. It always makes me feel a little under scrutiny, but overall I can't dismiss the potential value of finding out what my patients really think about me. Some of the questions are about general matters, such as telephone access and how long it takes to get an appointment. Others are more directly targeted towards the patient's interactions with the doctor, and contributors are specifically invited to comment on the experience of their most recent consultation.

When the collated results are emailed to me, I eagerly read them through. Being a good doctor isn't just about being popular, but I can't pretend that I wouldn't feel thoroughly demoralised if all my patients reported in their questionnaires that they hated me!

This year, the first question asked whether the doctor helped them feel at ease. Phew, 85 per cent of my patients felt I had done this. The second question was whether the patient felt that their concerns had been listened to: 83 per cent scored me highly on this one. A further 88 per cent of the respondents were impressed with my ability to communicate with them. It was a relief that I was scoring well, but I was only reaching the average scores

27

that most GPs achieve on these standardised surveys. Despite the regular pounding we get in the media, overall satisfaction in GP services remains consistently high.

The final question asked if the patients felt that their last consultation had helped lead to an improvement in their physical or mental health. On this I scored 40 per cent. Ouch! That meant for the majority of my patients, although they were put at ease, had their concerns listened to and were well communicated with, their actual health was no better off after seeing me than it was before.

This might seem like an epic failure, but actually it is a very accurate description of what a doctor does. The famous French writer Voltaire said that 'the art of medicine consists in amusing the patient while nature cures the disease'. I would add that nature sometimes makes them worse too, but ultimately our role is often to offer a distraction while time and the miraculous natural healing abilities of the human body work their magic. Some of my patients are very aware of the limits of my therapeutic abilities, but others seem to feel that I should be performing miracles. Regardless of their expectations of my curative powers, every patient expects me to be nice to them.

It sounds obvious really, and of course it is, but a huge proportion of complaints against doctors aren't about medical errors leading to ill health, but rather about doctors communicating poorly or not listening. One of my colleagues in A&E tells me that he always makes an effort to be ridiculously attentive to his patients however exhausted or frustrated he feels. Regardless of how rude, demanding and ungrateful the patient, he makes a huge show of bending over backwards to be gregariously charming. 'Speaking to patients is like acting,' he told me. 'The only difference between me and a film star is that I'm too short, fat and bald for Hollywood.' I try to follow his advice, but often my acting lets me down. It can be hard to be incessantly charming for an entire 12-hour night shift, but when I do manage it, my patients love me, regardless of how little I actually improve their health. This is why medicine is so often described by those in the profession as an art rather than as a science.

Having established the overwhelming importance of good communication skills when interacting with patients, it can be astonishing to witness some health-care professionals doing it so badly. Most catastrophic is when they have absolutely no idea how bad they are. Perhaps the oddest example I ever came across was as a student sitting in with a vascular surgeon. A nervous-looking gent in his 60s shuffled in with some smoking-related damage to the arteries in his legs. The very pompous surgeon asked him if he was still smoking. Defensively, the gent reassured the doctor that he had cut down from 20 cigarettes per day to just five. 'Hmm,' said the surgeon. 'That's hardly the greatest of achievements now is it? If I was a rapist who used to rape 20 women a day, but I had just recently cut down to raping just five women a day, I'd still be a horrible little rapist now wouldn't I?' The poor patient simply nodded aghast and I meanwhile had to pick my chin up off the floor. Perhaps it helped the patient in question give up those last five cigarettes, but even so, I'm not sure it could ever be recommended as a suitable technique for offering health promotion.

My personal worst moment of communication was about eight hours into a busy A&E shift some years ago. Corresponding to each patient sitting in the waiting room was a small set of paper notes headed with their name and the medical complaint that had brought them into the emergency department. Hour after hour, the routine was the same: I would pick up the top set of notes from the endless pile, walk into the noisy waiting room and shout out their name. For some reason, on this one occasion, instead of calling out the name, I shouted out the patient's medical complaint instead.

'SWOLLEN FACE,' I bellowed at the top of my voice.

I was absolutely mortified as this was a terrible, if accidental, breach of patient confidentiality. Oddly enough, though, the patients didn't seem to bat an eyelid and up stood a gentleman at the back of the waiting room with an impressively swollen face. He then proceeded to trudge unperturbed through into the treatment area. My terrible violation of his privacy had gone completely unnoticed, although I do wonder whether if I had shouted out 'TWISTED TESTICLE' or 'FOREIGN OBJECT IN ANUS' to a full waiting room, the fallout might have been rather more noticeable.

It's not just doctors who can be so horrendously insensitive. I once heard of a young couple going to have the all-important 20-week ultrasound scan of their first pregnancy. The sonographer performing the scan apparently kept looking at the screen while 'tut-tutting' loudly and shaking her head. The understandably anxious parents-to-be asked what was wrong. However, the sonographer replied that she couldn't possibly say, but that she would book them an appointment with the consultant for a few weeks' time. The dad at this point, in his own words, 'lost it a bit' and demanded the sonographer tell them what she could see. Astonishingly, her response was, 'Well, you know those funny people you sometimes see in the street? You know like those Oompa Loompa midgets in that *Willy Wonka* film. Well I think your baby might be one of those.' The disgusted parents demanded to see the consultant straight away who quickly reassured them that the scan was in fact normal and also reassured them that the sonographer wouldn't be doing any more baby scans!

Maggie III

Maggie phones me up quite often in the middle of the day when she finds herself alone and scared. I'm honoured that she confides in me, but I can't deny that I find our conversations difficult. I can't make everything fine with a prescription or a referral to a specialist. I spent so many years studying how to make people better that I still find it hard to accept that some patients are only going to get worse.

'How are things?'

It always seems an awkward question to ask someone who is dying. It's not like she's going to say, 'Brilliant thanks, Doc', but I'm yet to find a more appropriate way of opening a conversation with her, so I stick with it.

'Actually, Dr Daniels, I think I've found a bit of peace with it all. Don't get me wrong; I'm not happy about dying from cancer. Far from it. If truth be told, I would love to have a few more years to wander about the place, but in the big scheme of things I can't really complain about the life I've had. There have been ups and downs, but mostly ups, and I did always say that I never really planned to get old. In fact, I'd have made the most appalling cantankerous geriatric, so all in all it's probably for the best that I won't be around to see that through!'

'Well, that's one way to look at it.'

'I'm worried about my husband Tony, though. He's not really handling things very well. He just can't really accept that I'm on my way out. He keeps looking up things on the internet trying to find miracle cures. Now believe me, I'd fucking love a miracle cure, but I'm no idiot. These quacks are just after our money and I know that my cancer can't just vanish with a few vitamin pills and an Indian head massage. I just want to spend this last time I have with people I love around me. I don't want to be chasing miracles that don't exist.'

'Have you told Tony how you feel?'

'I can't bear to crush his hope. He needs hope to deal with this. It is his focus and at the moment it's the only thing driving him on. The latest one is this bloody ridiculous essential oils diet. I have to drink these oils he's bought on the internet and then mix them with organic celery and carrot juice. It's not exactly what I'd choose as my last supper, I can tell you. When he's out I get my daughter to sneak me in some fried chicken and doughnuts!'

'I think you need to tell Tony how you feel. You need to be really honest with him.'

'My husband's not one of those sorts of men, Dr Daniels. He doesn't really like to talk about his feelings. I'm sure he'd just clam up.'

'Funnily enough, my wife might say the same about me, Maggie, but here we are talking about some quite intimate, personal things. Sometimes you just have to try and see what happens.'

'I'll give it a go over the weekend and give you a ring on Monday to let you know how it goes.'

Maggie IV

'Hello, I'm here to see Maggie.'

'Come on in, Doctor. She's just having a facial done, but go on through as the make-up girl is just finishing up.'

It seemed odd to think of Maggie having a facial. I always considered her a robust Yorkshire lass and had never associated her with beauty regimes. As I entered the room, Maggie was getting the last of her blusher applied. I'm no expert on such matters, but it looked a bit overdone to me. Her cheeks were excessively rosy and her lips a dazzling ruby red. The young girl applying it looked up and gave me a smile. 'The family are coming to visit soon so we want her to look nice, don't we?' She added those final dabs of blusher with genuine pride, although I did rather wonder if there might be good reason why she only applied make-up to the deceased rather than to the living.

Despite the make-up girl's best efforts, Maggie still had the yellow tinge all corpses seem to have. I'd come to complete the paperwork, and as the last doctor to see her alive I was supposed to do a final examination of her body. Maggie had been at the undertakers since Saturday afternoon and it was now Monday

33

morning. If my examination revealed anything other than a diagnosis of death, something had gone very, very wrong.

I nodded at the undertaker to confirm that it was definitely Maggie lying on the metal trolley in front of me. I left my stethoscope in my bag, but stuck on some gloves and had a prod between her ribs on the left side of her chest to make sure she didn't have a pacemaker fitted. I knew Maggie's medical history well enough to know she didn't have one, but I checked just in case. We are always told that cremating a body with a pacemaker still inside can blow up the crematorium. I imagine this is in fact a bit of an exaggeration and it's more likely that the grieving relatives don't really want to find the remnants of charred batteries while spreading the deceased's ashes over her favourite rose bushes in the back garden.

I did mention to the undertaker that Maggie had had a silicone breast implant following her mastectomy some years before. There is no risk that the implants will blow up the crematorium, but they do leave a damaging sticky goo on the walls of the incinerator. Nowadays, most undertakers will remove them, which was an idea that tickled Maggie when she was alive. She told me she had suggested to her husband that he put her implant on the mantelpiece next to the urn containing her ashes, but apparently he hadn't found it funny.

I was going to miss Maggie. She had an amazing spirit that shone through and she always made me smile however gloomy our discussions. For all the amazing medical breakthroughs of modern years, once she received her diagnosis, all we ended up offering her were steroids and morphine. Both are cheap old-fashioned drugs that we've been using for decades. In their defence, the morphine gave her a pain-free death and the steroids probably gave her an extra couple of weeks. Maggie had promised me that she would try to open up to her husband, talk about her feelings and say goodbye to him. In the end, her condition deteriorated very quickly and just two days after she made me that promise she was gone.

For those last few weeks I was Maggie's confidant. I was someone outside the family to whom she could talk and on whom she could rely when she was in genuine need. It isn't something ever taught at medical school. It can't be measured or turned into a government target, but for those six weeks Maggie was my most important patient and although I was unable to cure her or prevent her death, nothing could make me feel more like a doctor than giving her my time.

When I'd heard the news of her death, I'd phoned her husband Tony to offer my condolences. I'd suggested that once the funeral was dealt with, he might want to pop in and have a chat. He didn't take me up on the offer, but a couple of weeks later he did leave an envelope for me at the reception. It was a photograph of Maggie looking young and carefree. Her head was tilted back and she was laughing at something. It really did capture her spirit beautifully. On the back it just said, 'Thank you for everything you've done for us, love Maggie and Tony.'

Can't be too careful

Tracey's entrance was never quiet. Buggy, shopping and three boisterous children piled into my room in a swirl of chaos.

''Allo again, Doc,' Tracey chirped cheerily. 'You must be sick of the sight of us, eh?'

'Not at all,' I fibbed back. 'So what brings you in today?'

'Well, it's all of us really,' and with that Tracey listed various transient minor ailments that seemed to be causing her and her brood great concern.

'This one's the worst,' she said, pointing at her son Bradley who was jumping most energetically off my couch. 'He's really poorly. Not himself at all. He's right off colour, he is. We was up the 'ospital all Saturday with him. 'Ad to call an ambulance and everything, but after nearly four hours waiting around in A&E they just said he had a virus and sent us home with paracetamol.'

Tracey spends a lot of time requesting medical attention. It seems that however many times either I or the other doctors offer reassurance, she needs more and will seek out medical help at the drop of a hat. I don't begrudge Tracey her frequent attendances. Well, if I'm honest, at the time I often do, but in the cold light of day I can accept that she is trying to be the best mum she can be. She worries about her children like all parents do, and she doesn't have the means to alleviate this anxiety without a trip to the doctor. For the last few years, I haven't really paid much heed to Tracey's frequent visits, but her name had now cropped up on our list of patients who attend A&E too frequently.

As we all know, the NHS has no spare money and one of the directives for saving funds is to persuade our patients to stop going to the hospital so often. For each attendance at the emergency department around £70 is charged to the NHS, and that cost doesn't change much whether the treatment is simply some gentle reassurance, as in the case of Tracey, or if 10 doctors wrestle to save your life after getting knocked down by a bus. Our GP surgery gets paid £65 a year to look after Tracey however many times she comes in. The simple logic is, therefore, that for minor ailments it is much cheaper for Tracey to see us at the GP surgery than for her to go to A&E. It also frees up time for the emergency doctors to see patients needing genuine emergency care! That is why my bosses were telling me to make an 'action plan' with Tracey in an attempt to prevent her from visiting the hospital so often.

After painstakingly reassuring Tracey that she and her children were going to survive the morning, I decided there was no time like the present and I was going to make the 'action plan' with her this very visit. We discussed all sorts of options to reduce her hospital attendances. I started by suggesting that she phoned the surgery rather than dial 999.

'But sometimes I ain't got no credit on my phone,' she replied.

'You could also take a taxi to the surgery rather than keep calling ambulances to go to A&E.'

'Taxi! How can I afford a bloody taxi?'

Finally, I proposed waiting for minor ailments to get better on their own, rather than instantly rushing to find a doctor.

'Thing is, Doctor, you can't be too careful,' she replied.

I printed out a copy of our 'action plan' and handed it to Tracey, but if I'm honest I didn't think it was going to make a great deal of difference to Tracey's attendance rate. It's easy to view frequent attendees like Tracey as time-wasters and malingerers, but the truth is that from this side of the fence it is very easy to label which emergency hospital attendances are appropriate and which aren't. GPs like me have the benefit of many years of medical training behind us to back up our decisions as to whether a patient needs to be seen in hospital – and we still often get it wrong! Tracey has no real support network and so she falls back on the medical profession. She is simply trying her hardest to keep herself and her family safe and for that I have to respect her.

I know that I'll get more letters from up above telling me that Tracey and her family attend A&E too often, but I think we just have to accept that some of the more vulnerable people in our society seek out our services to compensate for the lack of local support around them. However frustrating this can be for medical staff and the accountants trying to balance the books, I can't see any real alternative. If an attempt is made to try to ration Tracey's medical visits, my big fear is that she would stay at home for that one genuine emergency that really needed our help.

Crackhead Kenny II

I didn't initially recognise Kenny when he came to see me. It had been a few months since he'd been a patient I'd seen high as a kite and handcuffed to a prison officer in A&E. We were now in the very different context of my GP surgery on a drizzly Monday afternoon. Kenny seemed very different too. His face looked greyer and older in the daylight, and although he tried to manage a smile, without the aid of his narcotic buzz he had lost his infectious grin.

'I wanted to come and see you 'cos you was nice to me that time when we met in the casualty department.'

'Oh, how did you know I worked here?'

'Well, since I've been out, I've been back to A&E a few times. I was asking after you and that big Scottish male nurse told me you worked here as a GP, so here I am.'

I tried to muster a smile, but I could tell that having Kenny as a regular patient was going to be hard work. I could just imagine Barry the charge nurse thinking it hilarious to direct Kenny to me.

'How long have you been out of prison?'

'Nearly a month now. I'm staying at a friend's, but I'm going to get myself sorted out this time. No more smack for me, Dr Ben. I'm going clean for good this time.'

'Great, so are you involved with the drug and alcohol team? Are they doing a rehab programme with you?'

'No, Doctor. They're all useless there. I won't 'ave nothing to do with them. You're the only doctor I trust. That's why I'm here. I want you to help me.'

I like being told that I'm a good doctor and even though I knew that Kenny was after something, I couldn't help but feel flattered by his compliments however loaded they might have been. I'm sure one of the reasons that I wanted to be a doctor was some sort of unhealthy need to be liked. Many medics are, like me, constantly searching to be appreciated, and some patients can't help but try to manipulate that flaw at times. When I first started as a GP, my trainer told me that wanting to be loved by everyone is an admirable trait in a Labrador or a prostitute, but it doesn't make for a good doctor. I had a feeling that Kenny was going to prove this to be true.

'I really want to make it work this time, Dr Ben. If I can just get off the crack I can get myself a place to live and a job and most importantly back in touch with my little girl. She needs her dad.'

Kenny looked up at a scribbled picture on my wall that my eldest had drawn for me.

'If you've got kids, Dr Ben, you'll understand how important it is that I stay off the crack right now.'

'Absolutely,' I said, still waiting for the but …

'But I just need something to get me off the crack. Just to settle me down a bit and stop me losing it. Not much … Just a few Diazzies and some Temazzies and Zoppies. In prison they gave me Pregabbies, so I could do with a few of those.'

Patients who take meds for their weak bladder or high blood pressure tend not to have pet names for their tablets. When someone affectionately shortens the names of their medications, it always worries me. Diazzies are diazepam, temazzies are temazepam and zoppies are zopiclone. The meds that Kenny were asking for are all addictive and can cause a sort of spaced-out stupor when abused. Pregabbies are pregabalin, which are a type of painkiller, but they can be crushed up and injected to cause a high.

'Kenny, what's the point of coming off one drug and replacing it with another? If you really want me to help you and you want to clean up, we need to work out a programme of getting you off all drugs. It's the only way.'

Kenny had been working hard to pull on my heartstrings, but as soon as it seemed that I might not prescribe him what he wanted, his lip started to curl and his voice was on the rise: 'But I came to see you 'cos I thought you were gonna help me.' He scowled at me.

'Come on, Kenny, we both know that there is no point in me prescribing new addictive drugs to take up the job of the old addictive drugs. You need a proper supervised detox as an inpatient.'

'But I want to come off the crack today. There's a wait for detox, so that's why I need a little something now, just to get me off the really bad stuff.'

I really wanted to believe that Kenny was serious about giving up his habit for good, but I knew from painful previous experience that many addicts either misuse their prescription drugs or simply sell them to get enough money for the harder stuff.

'I won't do it, Kenny. The drug and alcohol team have a walk-in service that's open this afternoon. You could go round there right now and see them.'

'I can't believe you are refusing to help me. If you don't prescribe nothing for me I'll be back to using crack tonight. I could be dead in a month. You'll have to live with that on your conscience.'

'You don't have to go back to using crack, Kenny. That's a

decision that you still have control over. If you really want to change your life around you can—'

I didn't manage to finish my last sentence as Kenny was already out the door and gone.

Army medical I

Lee was here for an army medical examination and looked very nervous. He was tall, but looked more like an oversized 15-year-old than an adult. The prospect of him becoming a soldier seemed ridiculous.

'Are you gonna have to stick your finger up my arse?' he stammered.

'What? No, Lee. Why would I need to do that?'

''Cos my mates told me you 'ad to have that done before you could get in the army.'

'They were winding you up, Lee. Although I can't vouch for what they do to you at military training college.'

Lee broke out into a broad smile, clearly very relieved by the fact that my finger and his anus would be remaining unacquainted.

'So you're terrified of the prospect of having a rectal exam from a doctor, but not scared of being blown up by a Taliban bomb in Afghanistan?'

'I'll be all right, sir.'

'I'm not your teacher, Lee; you don't have to call me sir.'

'Oh right, yeah, sorry, Doctor.'

It felt like child abuse agreeing to let this 18-year-old boy go to war. My job was just to fill in a form declaring any previous medical history that the army might want to know about. Nobody really cared about my opinion on the war and the effect it might have on this poor boy.

'Lee, are you sure you want to join the army?'

'Yes, sir, I want to serve my country,' he said proudly.

'But do you really know what could happen out there. Do you even know what they're fighting about?'

'It's about 9/11 and what Osama bin Laden did and that ... and my mum says that joining the army will keep me out of trouble.'

That seemed a fairly stark reflection of life in modern Britain. Lee's mum clearly felt that going to Afghanistan would get him into less 'trouble' than letting him stay here and hang out on the local council estate.

I started scanning through his notes hoping to find some sort of ailment that might be picked up on by the army doctors who would review my report. A few childhood illnesses and some more recent weekend A&E visits were all that I could see. The previous month Lee had fractured his fifth metacarpal, a hand injury that is almost always caused by punching someone. The other injury four months earlier was a 'periorbital haematoma' (a black eye), again, most likely resulting from fighting.

Maybe Lee's mum was right. Maybe the army would be the best thing for him. He is from a really rough part of town and he has minimal education, and no skills or qualifications, not to mention that there really aren't many jobs going at the moment. His brother has been in a lot of trouble with the law and perhaps the army would stop Lee heading in the same direction.

'You sure you don't want me to say you've got flat feet or asthma or something? There must be something else you can do other than go into the army?'

'No thanks, sir, I'll be all right.'

I asked Lee to sign the form and with great concentration he wrote his name in a mixture of capital and small letters. His writing was that of a six-year-old and I could see why he didn't feel able to go on to college.

Some doctors refuse to refer patients for abortions due to religious and moral objections. I could probably do the same for army medicals, but it would be a pointless gesture that would only put extra work onto the other doctors at the practice.

As I stamped the form, Lee beamed me a big smile.

'You look really happy, Lee. You must be looking forward to joining up.'

'What, oh yeah, I definitely am, Doctor, but mostly I'm just pleased you didn't have to stick your finger up my arse.'

Tummy aches

Tracey was in, yet again. I was also still receiving letters stating that she and her family were attending the emergency department too frequently, but I'd long since given up on trying to persuade Tracey not to visit so often. The latest hospital attendance was for 'tummy aches' in six-year-old Bradley and it was for that same reason that Tracey had brought him in to see me today.

'They said up in A&E that they didn't know what was wrong with him and to visit you instead,' Tracey said.

Bradley was sitting sullenly in the chair rather than tearing around the room, which was out of character.

Once upon a time I had wanted to be a paediatrician and had spent a fair bit of time working on the children's ward as a junior doctor. I could usually fathom out the cause of tummy pain in kids and I was confident that Bradley's case would be no exception. I asked Bradley and his mum all about his symptoms. I asked about diarrhoea or constipation and if it hurt when he went for a wee. I asked if he was vomiting or had a fever and I made sure his glands weren't up. I spent some time prodding his tummy, but it didn't feel out of the ordinary, and when I tested his urine it was completely normal.

The next step was to ask about school. 'Are any of the other children nasty to you at school?' I asked. 'Are you being bullied?' Bradley shook his head.

'He's got loads of mates at school, Dr Daniels,' Tracey butted in. 'He loves school, but the teacher says he's sitting out of games more and gets tired more easily.' Bradley nodded gloomily in agreement at this. I got Bradley to get on the scales and when I plotted his weight on his growth chart it was dropping off a bit. Weight loss in children is a real worry and I urgently organised some more tests.

Within a couple of weeks Bradley had been for blood tests, X-rays and an ultrasound scan. Everything came back completely normal. I was relieved that Bradley didn't have leukaemia, which had been my initial fear, but he was still having tummy aches and wasn't himself. Most six-year-olds will complain of tummy aches at some point or another, but usually it doesn't last once they are distracted by something fun. I asked Tracey to bring in Bradley to get weighed regularly by our nurse and it was this that led to a breakthrough.

'He's hungry,' our practice nurse said to me triumphantly one morning after Bradley had been in.

'Who's hungry?'

'Bradley, that boy you've been worried about. He's having tummy aches because he's hungry. That's also why he's stopped growing and losing weight and why he's had no energy. It was obvious really. I asked Tracey about what he's been eating and it turns out she's been having problems with a debt collector and hasn't been able to afford to buy food. She's got herself in a right mess with it all and hasn't told anyone.'

I had asked Bradley and his mum about every possible symptom and ordered a multitude of medical tests. But I hadn't even considered asking if there was food in the house. Bradley wasn't such a medical mystery after all. He was suffering from something unfortunately felt by millions of six-year-olds across the world. There was a famine in Tanzania when I was working out there and I saw hundreds of malnourished, hungry children. It just wasn't something I was expecting to see in modern Britain. Our brilliant practice nurse Brenda had already put lots of things in place to help. The Citizens Advice team were working on resolving the debt issues and a charity was going to help with food donations until the family's social worker helped sort out Tracey's finances.

Bradley was an example of how easy it can be to give a medical diagnosis for what is actually a social problem. I wonder how many times I have labelled the misery of long-term poverty as clinical depression, and I once nearly diagnosed an old farm worker with eyesight problems, when the real reason he couldn't read my chart was that he had never been taught to read. I see poverty on a daily basis, but never thought that I would see malnutrition in a six-year-old boy in Britain. We live in one of the richest countries in the world and food here is plentiful. I would like to think that Bradley was a one-off case, but as everyone is becoming increasingly squeezed financially, I fear that he may well not be.

Glass test

My first experience of treating children was during my third year at medical school. It is at this time that we are allowed into the hospital to start seeing real-life patients. This is an exciting time for us as medical students, but there is always a fear that we will be asked difficult questions by a scary consultant on the ward round. This was the situation we found ourselves in as we started our first attachment to a paediatric department. Everyone had been very friendly up until now, but we had just started a ward round with Dr Bowskill. He was an odd man, most memorable for his 1970s side parting and very thick glasses with large brown frames. He looked more like an Open University physics lecturer than a doctor who needed to interact with small children and anxious parents.

My friend Jess and I were on his ward round and shuffled along behind him as he mumbled incoherently to the parents of the various children on the ward. We were mostly ignored until we reached the bed of a young boy with a rash.

'Now medical students, this boy has a rash,' he declared excitedly and then peered closely at the boy's skin through his jam jar-sized lenses. 'Fortunately for him this isn't a meningitis rash, but what test might we use to see if it was?'

Dr Bowskill turned to Jess.

This is easy, I thought. Everyone has heard of the glass test. I was sure Jess would know how to hold a glass against the skin to see if the rash disappeared under pressure. Unfortunately, it was becoming apparent that she hadn't ever heard of the glass test. Her expression was completely blank and she clearly didn't have a clue how to answer Dr Bowskill's question.

Rather than put Jess out of her misery or turn to me for the answer, Dr Bowskill just kept staring at her in silence. This silence just kept going and going and going, but Jess's expression continued to remain completely blank. *Come on Jess.* I was trying to transmit the answer into her brain using telepathy, willing to try anything to end this excruciatingly awkward silence. If she'd just looked up at me I could have mouthed the answer but she just continued to stare vacantly at the small red spots on the boy's arm.

After what seemed like an eternity, Dr Bowskill took off his glasses and handed them to Jess with great dramatic intent. 'Perhaps these might help?' he suggested in a loud, patronising voice.

Jess took the pair of glasses in her hand and I was sure she would click that she just had to hold the glass lens of his spectacles against the rash on the boy's skin and end this whole tortuous affair. But Jess continued to look just as vacuous, holding those glasses in her hand. I could see her getting increasingly desperate. In a final moment of panic she put the spectacles on her nose and peered closely at the boy's arm. She then looked up, shook her head and said, 'Nope, still don't know.'

At this point I absolutely fell about laughing. The painful awkwardness of the long silence accompanied by the hilarious sight of Jess wearing these ridiculous old-fashioned glasses was just too much for me to bear. Jess started laughing as well, still absolutely clueless of the relevance of the glasses to the whole meningitis diagnosis but aware that putting them on her nose in case she might be able to see the rash better had clearly not been Dr Bowskill's intention. Particularly as the strength of the lenses meant that she could see practically nothing at all.

Mr Lorenzo

By far my least favourite part of being a junior doctor was covering the medical wards at night. As darkness fell, one or two of us would be on duty to cover any potential emergencies that might crop up in any of the many medical wards that were spread over several floors of the hospital. I say emergencies – the reality was that many of the jobs were far more trivial. The nurses wanted us to rewrite a drug card or re-site a drip. Occasionally, though, a call would come through on my bleeper that wasn't quite so routine.

'I need you to prescribe something for one of our elderly gentlemen,' the nurse was saying. 'Something to calm him down sexually.'

'Eh?'

'Is there anything you can prescribe to reduce his testosterone levels or something?'

'What, you want me to chemically castrate one of your patients at 3 a.m. on a Sunday morning. What is he doing?'

'He keeps touching all of the nurses up. He rings his call bell every five minutes and as soon as we come anywhere near his bed, or the one next to him, for that matter, he reaches out his hand and grabs whatever he can.'

'Can't you tell him not to?'

'He doesn't understand English.'

When I arrived at the ward in question, I was greeted by a group of very irate looking nurses who led me over to the gent causing all the problems. Mr Lorenzo looked too frail and decrepit to be creating such a debacle, but as the nurse in charge escorted me over to his bed, sure enough, he made a grab for her behind. Clearly ready for this, the nurse nimbly dodged his flailing hand and gave him a hard stare. Mr Lorenzo looked at me, gave me a wink and then let loose a massive toothless grin and cackle.

'You mustn't touch the nurses,' I told him firmly.

'Funnily enough, we've tried telling him that. He only speaks Italian.'

'No touchee the nurseees,' I tried again, this time shouting in English but with a terrible Italian accent.

In the very unlikely scenario that Mr Lorenzo did understand me, he chose to ignore me and instead continued to give me his toothless grin before this time trying to grab the bosoms of a health-care assistant who had foolishly strayed within his groping range.

'Senore Lorenzo, por favori, no touchee. No touchee!' I shouted firmly. I then turned around and decided to stride away purposefully as if I had successfully resolved the issue when of course I hadn't. The nurses didn't bother waiting for me to be out of earshot before loudly commentating on how bloody useless I was.

I'd almost forgotten about Mr Lorenzo when about an hour later I got a frantic call from the nurse back on Mr Lorenzo's ward.

'It's Mr Lorenzo. He's fallen out of bed and he's unconscious.'

I ran to the ward to find the nurse in charge in floods of tears. They had become so fed up with Mr Lorenzo's constant bell ringing and subsequent groping that, despite it being against the rules, they had moved his call bell just out of his reach. He had reached and reached to try to get it and had fallen out of bed. Sure enough, down on the floor Mr Lorenzo was lying on his back, motionless and grey.

'I think he might be dead,' blubbed one of the nurses.

'We'll all lose our jobs,' another wailed.

'Stop crying and help me check for a pulse,' I interrupted.

We all stood over the moribund Mr Lorenzo, then just as the nurse in charge leaned over to try to find a pulse in his neck, as if by magic, his arm sprung into life and reached up her skirt. He opened his eyes, gave me that toothless grin and a wink and the rest of us collapsed into relieved laughter. So relieved were the nurses that they weren't going to have to explain to a coroner's inquest how they had moved his call bell out of reach that they happily tolerated his wandering hands for the rest of the night; well, for an hour or two at least.

Pseudoseizures

A pseudoseizure is a pretend fit. The person flails their arms and groans a bit as if having a real epileptic seizure, but in fact they are completely conscious and are in full control of their actions. This may seem to you as a very odd thing to do, but surprisingly they are really quite common. In fact, when I qualified as a doctor I witnessed three pseudoseizures before I saw a genuine epileptic fit. As I have become more experienced, it becomes easier to differentiate between a pseudoseizure and a real one.

Barry, the nurse I work with in A&E, is particularly unsympathetic to the condition. When he sees one of our regulars coming in pretending to be fitting, he rubs his knuckles hard on the patient's chest. If the patient sits bolt upright and tells him to 'fuck off', we can all be reassured of the true diagnosis. Personally I prefer a slightly subtler approach. By gently stroking the eyelash, someone conscious won't be able to help but flicker their lower lid. It avoids unnecessary swearing or potentially bruising the chest wall of some poor bugger who is genuinely having a seizure.

As an A&E doctor, I viewed pseudoseizures as yet another odd preserve of the crazies who dog the department, but as a GP I have been given the opportunity to gain some insight as to why people have them.

Carrie has them frequently, and recently she had one in my surgery waiting room. Picture the scene: Carrie comes to the desk wanting to see me on a busy Monday afternoon. The receptionist tells her that there are no appointments until the following day. Carrie then falls to the floor dramatically and shakes all her limbs. Everyone in the busy waiting room clambers over to help her and I get an emergency call interrupting both myself and the patient I am seeing. As I rush into the waiting room, I think I can see just the faintest of self-satisfied smiles on Carrie's face. She has got the attention she was craving. If the waiting room had been empty, I could have told Carrie to get up and stop making such a scene. This of course looks a tad on the unsympathetic side to her worried audience who are expecting me to offer suitable emergency treatment for what they believe to be a poorly epileptic.

I compromise and help Carrie into my room, apologetically upending the poor patient I had been seeing and delaying the remainder of my afternoon surgery. Carrie gets my attention and the appointment she wanted at rapid speed.

Her pseudoseizures also commonly occur when her boyfriend splits up with her or when she has had a big row with her mum. In these situations, the pseudoseizures are a brief and effective distraction from the current unpleasant realities of her life. They also result in her receiving the sort of sympathy and attention that she normally struggles to elicit. Carrie offers plenty for a psychotherapist to get stuck into, but for a lowly GP like me it is just a matter of trying to manage the situation as best as possible in the 10 minutes I have. I do feel sympathetic towards Carrie and hope the psychotherapist I referred her to helps her to manage her symptoms. Having said that, I can't say there aren't moments when I wish I had Barry at hand to offer a couple of hard knuckle rubs on her sternum the next time she dramatically collapses in my busy waiting room.

Antibiotic resistance

The national newspapers today are full of reports on the worrying increase in resistance to antibiotics and the potential return to an era when we have no discernible medical treatment to use against severe bacterial infections. The following is how antibiotic resistance was explained to me at medical school. I'm not sure who first came up with the comparison, but the concept can be best explained by thinking in terms of straightforward evolution:

A farmer has a problem with rabbits (think bacteria) eating crops on his field. He employs a few hunting dogs (think antibiotics) to kill the rabbits. Initially it is a great success and the rabbits are almost all gone. The farmer's crops are growing healthily and the farmer celebrates, assuming that rabbits will never be a problem again. He declares a great victory (think the remarks in the 1940s by doctors who thought that the days of infectious diseases were over). However, not all the rabbits are killed. Like all groups of organisms, there is variety. The few rabbits still alive are the ones that are the fastest and have the best hearing. These rabbits can hear the dogs coming and outrun them. These remaining 'super rabbits' breed with each other (like rabbits) and soon all the rabbits on the farm are extra fast and have great hearing. The old hunting dogs can't kill any of them, so effectively the rabbits have 'developed resistance'.

The farmer decides to get some new dogs, which are even faster and can hunt very quietly (think newer antibiotics). Initially the new dogs are killing the rabbits despite their speed and good hearing; however, one or two of the rabbits are brown rather than white and the dogs can't see them very well. These remaining brown rabbits breed with each other and soon all the rabbits are brown and the dogs can't see them (think super-infections such as MRSA and C. diff). This cycle continues, with the farmer continually trying to adapt his dogs to keep his farm healthy. The rabbits aren't being cunning or clever. They are simply evolving and reacting to the environment which is being manipulated by the farmer.

The other issue the farmer notices is that the dogs cause other problems. They occasionally kill some of his hens (think unwanted side effects). He also finds that when his dogs have killed lots of the rabbits, there is suddenly more food and space for the mice, so they now flourish. The mice now become pests themselves (think fungal infection such as thrush).

Sometimes the farmer sees that his crops are being eaten and assumes it is the rabbits. In fact, this time it is a caterpillar infestation (think viruses) eating his crops for which the dogs are of absolutely no help. He foolishly sends out his dogs again even though the rabbits aren't the culprits. The farmer has given himself all the problems that the dogs cause without any of the advantages. This is what happens when we give antibiotics for viral infections such as colds. We cause resistance and inflict side effects without helping clear the infection. After the farmer sends the dogs out, the caterpillars turn into butterflies and fly away leaving the crops to recover. This recovery had nothing to do with the dogs, but foolishly the farmer just sees his crops recuperating and assumes that his dogs are the saviours. He sends out his dogs every time the caterpillars arrive not realising that they are causing more harm than good to a problem that is self-resolving.

The other issue is that the rabbits can now spread directly to the neighbour's farm. When they do so, the neighbouring farmer brings in his old dogs, but the rabbits are already superfast, have excellent hearing and outstanding camouflage. His dogs have no hope and soon the rabbits have overrun his farm and all the neighbouring farms. The good old rabbits from a few years ago don't even exist any more and so all the farmers have to try to find new, special expensive dogs to try to deal with any sort of rabbit infestation. Eventually the farmers concede defeat, realising that they won't ever be able to keep up with the rabbits' constant adaptation.

This is the losing battle that the medical profession is fighting every day. There is no long-term solution. Pharmaceutical reps travel the nation promoting their companies' latest erectile stimulant or antidepressant but they never try to sell us their new antibiotic because the drug companies have stopped making them. There hasn't been a new one for a decade or so. Pharmaceutical companies don't want to invest money into developing new antibiotics because they know that there will be resistance too quickly for them to be of any real selling value. When I first qualified just a few years ago, ciprofloxacin used to be a special antibiotic that was still considered to work against all bugs. It was akin to the best china that would only be brought out on special occasions so that it wasn't ruined. It was expensive and there was a real push to use it as little as possible so that bugs didn't develop resistance to it. I seem to remember that in the hospital I worked in you had to be a consultant to prescribe it. Ciprofloxacin is still a good antibiotic, but it is as cheap as chips now and is prescribed quite readily by GPs and junior hospital doctors. I regularly see urine infections that are resistant to ciprofloxacin and there isn't really an alternative. The best china is faded and chipped now and there isn't likely to be any great investment in a new set.

In hindsight it could be considered immensely arrogant of the human race to think that we could control bacteria and eliminate them from harming us. Bacteria are the oldest living organisms on earth, having been around for billions of years. They have adapted through a multitude of changing environments from hot and cold to dry and wet. Their ability to mutate and adapt means that they have outlasted many millions of plant and animal species that could not keep up with the changing environment. In the 1940s, when antibiotics arrived, bacteria were probably sitting around thinking: 'Hey boys, these antibiotics are a pain in the arse, but if we mutated through that Ice Age of 10,000 BCE and the great volcano season of 1 million BCE, this is nothing.' I'm sure bacteria will adapt to survive many more changes and challenges and will still be around many millions of years after the human race has disappeared.

Doctors now talk about preparing for a post-antibiotic era. This will be when all the common bacteria are resistant to all antibiotics and we will simply have to rely on our immune systems again. For those among us who are fit and healthy adults this will probably be okay. However, for the elderly or very young, or those who have weakened immune systems for whatever reason, this will be disastrous. Infectious diseases could once again become our most common cause of death, taking over from cancer and heart disease.

To be fair, simple antibiotics do still work against many simple infections. We still are within the 'antibiotic era' and some good old-fashioned penicillin should still treat a good old-fashioned bout of bacterial tonsillitis. (When the GP says please finish your course of antibiotics, please don't stop after two days because you're feeling a bit better. This is how the resistance gets a hold.) Things are getting better. Patients increasingly understand the limitations of antibiotics and most GPs try to avoid prescribing antibiotics unnecessarily. Although we probably still prescribe vastly more antibiotics than are strictly necessary, some reports have suggested that GP antibiotic prescribing rates are down 50 per cent in the last decade. Well done us! Our slightly more frugal antibiotic prescribing does seem to have helped stem resistance rates.

If you catch a bacterial infection in Portugal, the chance of the bug being resistant to antibiotics is much higher than if you picked up the same type of bug here in the UK. This is almost certainly because in much of southern Europe, antibiotics can be bought over the counter without a prescription. In countries where this is the case there is a strong culture of popping to the local chemist and buying a couple of days' worth of antibiotics if you're feeling a bit peaky, no matter what the cause. This has led to antibiotic resistance flourishing. Other common offenders are those elements of the farming industry who often blanket treat their cattle with antibiotics in an attempt to ward off disease and keep their profit margins up.

Having said all this, you may be surprised to hear that GPs still prescribe far too many of them when not necessary. 'Why?' I hear you shout. Basically it is because many patients still expect and demand them and at times it can be really difficult to say no. Some patients feel cheated, wronged and angry if they leave the surgery without them. They storm out, slam the door and go to A&E, where they lengthen the waiting times and eventually get the antibiotics they want from the exhausted, broken A&E doctor who is so worried about breaching the four-hour wait targets that he doesn't have the energy to say no.

Here is an example:

Me: 'Good afternoon Mr Jones. How can I help today?'

Patient: 'I've got a sore throat, a dry cough and a blocked nose.'

Me: 'Hmm, well after listening to your chest and looking at your throat and ears it would appear that you have a nasty viral upper respiratory tract infection also known as a cold.'

Patient: 'Thought as much, Doc. If I can just have a course of antibiotics, I'll be out of your hair. I can see how busy you are today.'

Me: 'Actually, Mr Jones, I don't think antibiotics will help because it's a virus you've got and antibiotics don't work against viruses.'

Patient: 'But I'm off to Tenerife on Thursday and I need to be better for that.'

Me: 'I do sympathise, Mr Jones, but the antibiotics don't work against viruses regardless of whether you are off on holiday or not.'

Patient: 'I see, so my taxes pay your salary, but you're too tight to fork out for a few lousy antibiotics.'

Me: 'It really isn't about money, Mr Jones, it's about what will and won't make you better.'

Patient: 'I've been getting antibiotics for my colds for years and I always got better. Why did those other doctors give me antibiotics?'

Me: 'Perhaps they were giving you what they thought you wanted. They were succumbing to your expectations and choosing the easy option. We all want our patients to like us and as a result doctors are guilty of having overprescribed antibiotics for years. I apologise for that. It is something that this current generation of GPs are trying to rectify by changing expectations and educating ...'

Patient: 'Well I think it's you that needs the educating 'cos you're a shit doctor and I'm off to A&E if I can't get my antibiotics from you.' [*Loud slam and no Christmas card.*]

If I had simply prescribed the antibiotics, Mr Jones would have left happy. I would have avoided the long stressful argument that made me run even later in my busy afternoon surgery. The cost of the antibiotics would have been a drop in the ocean compared to my overall drug budget, and in the growing worldwide crisis of antibiotic resistance, one more course of amoxicillin probably wouldn't have made a huge difference. Mr Jones would have given me positive feedback in my patient satisfaction questionnaire and this would have made me look like a 'good doctor'. Nevertheless, I was a better doctor for saying no.

Diabetes

Type 2 diabetes is a disease that GPs are seeing more and more of, and recent research suggests that treatment will use £16.9 billion of the NHS budget, as the number of diabetics rises from 3.8 million to 6.25 million by 2035. This has fuelled scaremongering in the media, with talk of 'diabetes bankrupting the NHS within a generation'.

Unlike other diseases, discussion about type 2 diabetes often results in debate about who is to blame. The head of diabetes UK states that the NHS needs to improve its care of diabetics. Other commentators recommend that the government should be blamed for not taxing sugar-rich food, while others suggest that supermarkets are responsible because of the cheap, unhealthy foods they push. The other obvious villains in the piece are the diabetics themselves, who are usually portrayed as unrepentant fatties who can't stop shovelling down the doughnuts. I'm not convinced that looking to blame any one group, especially those who have the condition, serves any purpose other than demonising the disease and alienating the sufferers.

Firstly, it's important to state that type 2 diabetes isn't solely caused by obesity. Age and genetics play a significant role, too.

Nevertheless, it is true that appropriate improvements in diet and lifestyle would cause incidence of the disease to plummet and would also significantly reduce complication rates for those who already have the condition.

Part of my job is to encourage an improvement in the lifestyle of my patients, but the more bullish I am about the advice I give, the more defensive and unresponsive my patients usually become. Early on in my career I remember having a hugely overweight patient who insisted that she only ate lettuce. When I suggested this couldn't be true, the ensuing debate escalated to a full-blown row. We got nowhere and on top of this, she disengaged from any of the support services available and completely failed to gain control of either her weight or her diabetes.

The longer I'm a doctor, the more I realise that patriarchal-style education rarely works with regard to encouraging lifestyle changes. As with any addiction, the addict needs to admit the problem to themselves before he or she can accept any help and change behaviour. Deep down, most of us have issues with food at some level and I am no exception.

I spend a lot of my time explaining the perils of excess sugar to my patients and so this particular week I had decided to practise what I preach. I completely banned myself from eating any sugar during my working day. How hard could it be? It was going well on Monday until one of my morning patients brought me a Twix bar. It sat on my desk goading me for half an hour, but then temptation got the better of me. The shiny gold wrapper poked out of the bin mocking my poor willpower for the rest of the morning. The afternoon was going well until our nurse brought in some home-baked chocolate brownies to celebrate her birthday. It seemed rude not try one and they looked so much more appetising than the pot of sunflower seeds

I had optimistically brought in to stave off the predictable mid-afternoon sugar craving ...

Changing diet and lifestyle habits that we have held for all of our lives is hard. Our brains are trained to respond positively to the reward of a sugary treat; well, mine is anyway.

Fortunately for my diabetic patients, we have a fantastic new community diabetes team. The nurses who run it are enthusiastic and welcoming and offer clear non-judgmental advice and support on everything related to diabetes. They don't preach or lecture but just allow patients to come and ask questions, meet each other, dispel myths and hopefully feel motivated to make the changes they need to control their disease.

Right now I'm slim, young and active, but I'm certainly not immune to getting diabetes one day. For those of you feeling 'holier than thou', who can live on a diet of porridge oats and celery, I salute you, but for the rest of us mere mortals let's look at some more practical ways of helping fight diabetes rather than solely looking to vilify the victims of the disease. I mentioned how brilliant our community diabetes team is, but I really wish we had a similar service to help overweight patients before they develop the disease. Practical, simple, non-judgmental support would be a real investment and potentially pay for itself many times over if it successfully reduced diabetes.

We do need to work hard together to effectively prevent and treat type 2 diabetes, but ultimately, if the NHS collapses it will do so because of underfunding and government privatisation. Let's not blame type 2 diabetics who already have enough on their plate (pun intended).

Tarig I

Tarig poked his tongue out at me and it was covered in a white fur.

'It's sore every time I eat,' he told me.

'It's a fungal infection on your tongue.'

'Is it because of my disease?'

'Yes, the HIV is affecting your immune system.'

He shrugged and went to stand up and leave.

'Still not going to consider taking any medications for it?'

'No, Doctor. You know that my fate is God's will, not yours or mine.'

It was now my turn to shrug. I nearly let him leave, but as a doctor it is so hard to watch a dying man walk away, knowing that he could be treated and effectively cured.

'It's not too late to change your mind, Tarig. On medication you could live a long and normal life.'

Tarig was a Coptic Christian from Egypt. He was a strictly religious man, but he slept with a prostitute while on a business trip to the Sudan and contracted HIV. Rather than accept treatment, he decided that the HIV was a punishment from God that he must suffer, even if this meant a painful, premature death.

As a teenager I used to get drawn into long religious debates with Jehovah's Witnesses who came knocking at the door. I was convinced that I would enlighten them as to what I believed to be the flaws in their religious convictions. They of course felt they could do the same for me. You won't be surprised to hear that after many wasted hours of debate on my doorstep, I had failed to convert a single Jehovah's Witness to atheism. As I've got older, my atheist ideas have remained, but now I wouldn't dream of challenging anyone else about their religious views, especially my patients. My job is to treat them within their cultural beliefs rather than inflict my own upon them, but this can be difficult when their viewpoint is affecting their physical health. I just couldn't bring myself to let go of Tarig.

'Tarig, when you're about to cross a busy road, do you look left and right first?'

'Yes, of course.'

'But surely if a car hits you that would be God's will too?'

'Yes, God will decide my fate, but he wants me to take some responsibility too. He wanted me to resist temptation when he sent the whore to cross my path, but I failed him and I must accept the consequences of my sin. I must suffer for my redemption.'

I felt a bit like the teenage me arguing in vain with the Jehovah's Witnesses. As a GP I've witnessed some of the enormous good religion can achieve. Some of my patients have given up drugs and crime in order to embrace the love of the Lord. Some of our local religious communities offer amazing support for members of their flock who are taken ill both physically and mentally. Faith can also help people overcome enormous personal suffering and help them move on and find meaning in their lives. I wasn't trying to convert Tarig to atheism; I simply wanted him to agree to take life-saving medications that were freely available at our local HIV clinic.

The last time I witnessed someone die of AIDS was 2002. He was a young man, barely out of his teens, and he was lying helplessly in filthy sheets in a Mozambique hospital. I can still picture the painful-looking sores eating into his lips and the skin cancers that had spread all over his body. Pneumonia was taking over his lungs, meaning he was gasping for breath. His broad shoulders showed how muscular he had once been, but now he was hunched over with his muscles all but completely wasted away. We gave him antibiotics to try to fight the infection but the HIV virus had completely destroyed his immune system. Each day on the ward round I saw him fade further away until he was almost a skeleton. Everyone was surprised how long he lasted. Finally, during my last week there, he gasped his last breath in front of my eyes.

Times have changed and now HIV is brilliantly managed by our local clinic. People living with HIV today can look forward to a normal life expectancy on treatment. Without treatment the condition is unpredictable and dangerous. I feel woefully out of my depth with Tarig, but while he continues to refuse to take treatment or be seen by the specialist, he is stuck with me, and I with him.

'Look, Tarig, let me at least treat the thrush on your tongue. I can give you some drops that will clear it. And can you let me do some blood tests so that we know at what stage your disease is?'

Tarig reluctantly agreed.

I documented again very carefully Tarig's decision to decline a referral to the HIV team and that he was of sound enough mind to make this choice. If he was genuinely going to die of this disease, I needed to make sure that I was able to protect myself medico-legally from any potential fallout.

Is the quality of NHS care really declining?

Late one evening 30 years ago, the senior partner at my surgery visited a six-year-old boy at home with a fever. He diagnosed a viral illness and advised paracetamol. By the next morning, the young lad was dead from meningitis. Mortified to hear of his mistake he visited the grieving family to apologise, but rather than being met with anger and legal proceedings, he was thanked by the tearful parents for his help and efforts the previous night – and he continued to be the family's GP for years to come.

The diagnosis of early meningitis is as difficult to make now as it ever was and it is still missed by doctors today, as it was 30 years ago. Losing a child to the disease is as horrendous as it always has been. The difference appears to be that expectations have changed. We don't yet have lawyers loitering around A&E waiting rooms or chasing ambulances, but there definitely appears to be an increased awareness that medical errors can lead to financial compensation and claims continue to increase year on year.

Annual NHS compensation payouts grew from £277 million in 2000/01 to almost £1 billion in 2010/11. This is partly related to the increase in the number of claims but also to the increased cost of the individual claims, which can be up to £10 million each.

Ironically, this increase is in part due to improved NHS care rather than an increase in errors. The young boy with the missed meningitis 30 years ago may well have survived today. The diagnosis may have still been missed early on, but improved intensive care facilities could have resulted in him surviving, albeit with severe brain damage and physical disabilities. The biggest compensation payouts are made to help financially support severely disabled children who may now live for several decades but remain in need of long-term expensive care packages.

So in these times of desperately low NHS resources, what can we do about expensive compensation payouts? The obvious answer is to reduce the number of cock-ups. This may seem simple enough, but unfortunately mistakes and errors will always happen. The causes are multiple and I am not trying to brush over or dismiss them. I am also not trying to excuse them or suggest that the NHS and its staff shouldn't be held accountable; I am simply stating that as long as health care is delivered by humans, errors will be made.

Every day the tabloid media offer terrifying tales of health-care blunders. It feels like a continuous drip-feeding of the idea that the NHS is broken and doomed to collapse. These stories feed fears that every operation will be botched and every medical decision made will be the wrong one. I don't begrudge compensation payouts when genuine mistakes have been made and I'm sure the families involved would rather have the good health of their loved one than a damages payment. However, it is important to recognise that the rise in the number of claims isn't due to standards of care in the NHS falling. We still have a long way to go, but here on the coalface, I genuinely think that overall the quality of care is improving.

As doctors, it is our job to learn from our mistakes, share them, be honest and open about them, and most importantly make sure they don't happen again. As patients, I would advise that you ask questions, share medical decisions with your doctor and educate yourselves about your own health and illnesses. Medical mistakes have been, are and will always be made, but fortunately genuine cases of medical negligence are still rare. The cynic in me wonders if the constant drip-feeding of medical error stories is an attempt to convince the public that the NHS is failing and therefore dampen down any opposition as widescale privatisation of the health-care system is sneaked in through the back door.

Jimmy Savile

The exposure of child abuse allegedly perpetrated by Sir Jimmy Savile was a massive shock to me. As a kid in the 1980s, I used to love *Jim'll Fix It* and was once greatly envious of those children who got to sit on his knee. Not any more. Although never my greatest hero (Daley Thompson wins that award), Savile was nonetheless an integral part of my childhood. A part that has now been completely tarnished.

Were I not a doctor, these allegations of abuse might have felt like a watershed moment for me. They might have ended a certain naivety bestowed upon me by the good fortune of a sheltered, happy and abuse-free childhood. As a medic, that innocence ended when I first set foot on a psychiatric ward a decade or so earlier. I was astounded at how many of the inpatients of both sexes had been abused as children or young adults. In medical school I had learned that mental illness was something that randomly afflicted people due to a combination of genetics and miss-firing neurotransmitters. I had been taught that in mental illness brain chemicals go wrong in the same way that chromosomes go wrong in Down's syndrome, or blood clotting doesn't work in haemophiliacs. Reading through the medical records of the female patients on the acute psychiatric ward, there was not a single one who had not suffered some sort of trauma as a child or young adult. Stories of sexual abuse, physical abuse, neglect and usually a combination of all three jumped out from almost every set of notes.

The psychiatrist in charge of the ward told me that she would be out of a job if she could somehow prevent anyone from ever being abused as a child. The psychiatric wards would be empty, she told me. Those wards weren't empty. They were in fact full to bursting with desperate, damaged, unhappy people and the constant pressure of more people needing to be admitted was always there. Now clearly not everyone abused ends up with a mental illness and not everyone with a mental illness was abused. I'm sure genetics and brain chemicals also play their part, but the association between childhood trauma and mental illness in adulthood is well documented. I wonder if those adults who do the abusing even consider just how much pain and torment they cause and just how long it lasts.

Most A&E departments have regular self-harmers who repeatedly present to the department with cuts on their arms that need stitching up. In A&E, we only asked for the details of what had happened that day and would often feel frustrated spending time mending what appeared to be self-inflicted injuries. Here in general practice, we get the whole life story and soon learn that although the cuts on the arms are self-inflicted, the underlying damage was probably meted out by an adult abuser some years earlier. As a doctor it doesn't necessarily make self-harm any easier a problem to manage, but at least it goes some way towards helping me understand it.

Of course, everyone's aim is to prevent children being abused. As with Jimmy Savile's victims, it has taken until adulthood before many of my patients have opened up to me about the abuse they suffered as children. My constant anxiety is about how many of my young patients are suffering abuse right now. Statistics would suggest at least one or two, which is a sobering thought and enough to persuade me to keep asking questions and stay vigilant.

There aren't many positives to take from the allegations that flooded the media following the exposure of Savile, but I hope that the current publicity might encourage us adults to remember how common child abuse is and to always bear it in mind when working with children and young people. Even more importantly, perhaps it will inspire one or two children to feel empowered enough to step forward and speak up about abuse they are suffering from right now. Many of us are wondering about the adults who were around during the 1970s, and asking how did they let it happen? Wouldn't it be a great shame if in 40 years from now people look back on this generation and ask the same thing?

Nathan

'I reckon I've got AIDS, Doctor.'

'Right, okay, erm ... what makes you think that?'

'Well, I think that I might have caught it the other night.'

'Did you sleep with someone you think might be at risk?'

'Well, up until last week I'd never had sex before, but I think something might have happened on Friday night.'

'Right, so what happened?'

'Well, I got really drunk. I remember being in a club and then my friends say they lost me for about half an hour until they found me asleep in the kebab shop with sick down me and took me home.'

'And are you worried you caught HIV that night?'

'Well, I don't remember you see, so I could have done. Anything could have happened in that half an hour.'

'Well, yes, in theory, I guess, but do you really think you might have slept with someone when you were in that state?'

'Might have done.'

I looked up at Nathan and wondered how I might put this without sounding mean.

'I guess what I'm trying to say, Nathan, is that isn't it a bit unlikely that you had sex in the half an hour between vomiting over yourself in a nightclub and then being found asleep in the kebab shop next door?'

Nathan looked at me blankly, as if this didn't seem very unlikely at all. I would never claim to understand the inner workings of the female mind, but I can't believe that any girl would consider a drunken, barely conscious Nathan covered in vomit to be sexually irresistible. I was really going to have to spell this out.

'I guess what I'm just trying to say is that isn't it a little bit improbable that you were able to meet a girl, chat her up, take her somewhere quiet and persuade her to have unprotected sex with you, while then managing to get back into the town centre and falling asleep in the kebab shop where your friends found you just 30 minutes later. All this while being so drunk that you could barely walk and were covered in vomit.'

Nathan did look a bit crushed. Perhaps I had overdone it a bit, although I did refrain from mentioning that in that sort of drunken stupor he was unlikely to have been able to get an erection. I really had pulled his story apart like a top lawyer laying into the defendant. Surely faced with such damning evidence, Nathan would crumble and accept that he probably didn't catch HIV that night.

'I still think I should have a test just to be sure. It would make me feel better.'

Under normal circumstances regular HIV tests are to be commended, but in Nathan's case I was worried that by giving him a test I was colluding with his health anxieties. Nathan's irrational fears about his health weren't new. A few months earlier he'd been convinced that his very benign looking mole was skin cancer and wouldn't be reassured until I sent him to see a dermatologist. He had also recently convinced himself he had a heart problem because he was sometimes aware of his heartbeat and so kept coming to see the nurse and demanding an ECG. In fact looking through the notes, Nathan was in the surgery almost every week.

We all worry about our health sometimes, but most of us have a sensible threshold as to when we need to seek medical help for our ailments. We are able to look rationally at our symptoms and decide how potentially serious they might be, and can usually reassure ourselves when they are obviously benign. Nathan doesn't seem to possess this ability. He could be called a hypochondriac, although this seems a slightly crude, old-fashioned description. I would say he has health phobias. He has an irrational fixed fear about his health that often takes over his life and is very debilitating. When Nathan presents with yet another ailment, my gut reaction is to attempt to reassure him. He knows that he worries excessively, but his overwhelming health fears trigger a niggling doubt in me. Like the boy who cried wolf, perhaps at one point Nathan will genuinely have something wrong that needs treating and I'll be the one that misses it.

Nathan and I became trapped in a *folie à deux*, in which he came to see me for reassurance and I encouraged his behaviour by offering him a test that gave him a brief respite from his fears when the result come back as normal. Round and round we went, but I decided it was going to stop today.

'Nathan, you don't need an HIV test because you don't have HIV. You're a healthy 17-year-old lad and you need to stop worrying about your health.'

'I reckon I'd just stop worrying if you gave me an HIV test.'

'I'm going to refer you to a therapist. To address your excessive health concerns. You need help to find ways to stop worrying about your health so much.'

Nathan looked at me blankly and then quietly left my room.

He didn't ever go to see the therapist I referred him to, but instead went and got an HIV test from the walk-in sexual health clinic. I guess that I ultimately failed in my plan to break the cycle, but on a more positive note Nathan does seem to be coming in to see me less frequently. Perhaps he's better at dealing with his health phobias. Or perhaps he's just given up on me and is sitting at home terrified that he is about to die from the latest of his perceived ailments.

Army medical II

It was a year after I had completed the army medical for Lee. He still looked like a young boy, but something had changed in him.

'I'm due to go back for my second tour in Helmand, Dr Daniels, but I don't want to go. Can you write something to say I can't go back?'

'I guess I can try. Was it really bad out there?'

'It was terrible. All my friends back here keep asking me is if I killed anyone. I don't even think I ever saw a Taliban to shoot at, let alone kill. All I saw on patrol were kids and women and old people, but every step you're wondering if a sniper is going to get you. Every time you see a kid you wonder if they're going to blow themselves up. They look at you like you're scum and the women shout at us in their language and spit at us. Being in the vehicles was even worse. Imagine being in a vehicle that gets blown up by an IED [improvised explosive device] and catches fire. You either stay inside and burn or you try to get out and a sniper shoots you.'

He went on: 'My mates think it sounds exciting, but I was scared the whole time even though most of the time nothing happens at all. Even during down time I couldn't relax. All the worrying made me ill. My bowels were all over the place and I barely slept.

93

Some of the other guys in the battalion took the piss out of me, but I know they were scared as well. I just can't go back there. Since I've been back I'm just angry all the time. Please don't make me go back.'

'Lee, I can try writing something, but ultimately it's the army doctors who get to decide, not me.'

I wrote a long letter stating that I believed Lee had post-traumatic stress disorder. They might dismiss it outright given that Lee hadn't really even seen much action, but he did have all the symptoms. He couldn't sleep, was having flashbacks and experiencing continually high levels of anxiety.

Lee was worried that I would think him a coward, but the thought didn't cross my mind. I've never been in the situation where my levels of bravery have been tested. Who knows how I'd cope in the environment of frontline Afghanistan, never being able to close your eyes and go to sleep without a little part of your brain knowing that a rocket could come flying through the window or a Taliban disguised as a police officer could shoot you while you slept. Why some people cope in that situation and others don't, I'm not sure, but Lee was my patient and he wasn't faring well. My letter concluded with the statement that I thought Lee was not safe for frontline duties and could be a danger to himself and his battalion. I hoped the army might believe me and give Lee a medical discharge.

Lee didn't have to wait to find out if the army would discharge him on medical grounds. He got into a fight with some local lads in the town centre and his punch put a 16-year-old boy in intensive care. He is on remand and looking at a likely one-year stretch in prison. I haven't seen him since, but his mum's optimism about him going into the army to keep him out of trouble seems a sad irony now.

Betty Ferrari

I was working in A&E again. As I arrived for my shift my heart sank as I spotted the queue of ambulances sat at the entrance. Each paramedic crew was patiently waiting to offload their patient into a department that was already completely full. Barry was in charge today, and he was looking very flustered as he tried to move trolleys in and out of cubicles in a gallant attempt to make space when there was none. The phones were all ringing at once and it felt like a scene from a disaster movie.

At times like this, each new patient being brought in feels like an extra mouth to feed when there is already not enough food to go round. The doctors and nurses collectively groan as they witness each new admission being wheeled in. The poor patient sitting on the ambulance trolley needs help, time and care, but this can often be lost when the staff are in such a flap simply trying to manage the impossible task of fitting 50 patients into a department with 30 beds.

'There's a bed crisis,' one of the nurses mouthed to me as if to try to explain the madness that I was walking into. There was a time when a bed crisis was considered to be a rare, traumatic event, but now we just seemed to run on the assumption that there was always a bed crisis, which makes the phrase meaningless.

Fortunately for me, I wasn't responsible for managing the bed issue. I was simply there as a foot soldier. My job was to see and treat the patients as effectively and efficiently as I could. I blanked out the noise and chaos and picked up the medical notes of the next patient to be seen. To my surprise it was a patient I knew very well and, if I'm honest, was probably my favourite patient at my practice. One of the odd perks of being both a GP and an occasional A&E doctor is that I sometimes meet my primary care regulars when they have an emergency and end up in casualty.

Betty was a great character, well known to all the staff at my practice. She had a loud cackling laugh and called everyone 'darling'. She made sure to buy the practice a bottle of sherry every Christmas and would flirt outrageously with any man aged between 16 and 100. Betty had worked the boards as a cabaret performer for years and I loved visiting her flat and seeing the old black-and-white photos of her from the late 1940s looking glamorous. Her stage persona was Betty Ferrari, which sounds like the name of a drag act now, but back in the late 40s, she assures me, it was alluring and exotic. 'I was married to the stage and I was monogamous!' That was her way of telling me that she never settled down or had children. With no family, Betty was lonely. I visited as often as I could. If we had medical students attached to the surgery I would bring them to meet her. I told them she had an interesting medical history but the real reason for the visit was because she loved the company and revelled in performing a few of the 'old numbers' for a new audience. Unfortunately, these days her bad lungs mean she rarely finishes a song without being interrupted by a coughing fit.

Back in those original photos the cause of her current suffering could be clearly seen. In each picture she was holding a cigarette holder with the cigarette itself shrouding her in a swathe of smoke.

'We used to think we were so sophisticated,' Betty told me, 'and I loved the sexy husky voice the smoke gave me.'

'You could still give up,' I often told her.

'Too late now, darling,' she would reply with her husky laugh.

It was no real surprise that Betty was here in hospital. She had been in and out of the emergency department seven times in the last six months. Each admission was for the same complaint. Her lungs just couldn't get enough oxygen into her blood stream. On each occasion she was admitted for a few weeks, given oxygen, steroids and antibiotics and then sent home. She had all sorts of inhalers, but despite everyone's best efforts, an infection would cause her lungs to deteriorate again and she would be back in hospital. We couldn't give her oxygen in her flat as she still smoked and so the risk of her accidentally igniting the oxygen supply and blowing herself up was too high.

Betty was sitting up on the trolley leaning forwards. She was struggling to breathe and had an oxygen mask tight round her face. She was in a hospital gown that covered her front but was left open at the back displaying her ribs and shoulder blades protruding through tired pale skin. Betty was so short of breath that she couldn't really answer my questions. She had been sitting in this cubicle for the last two hours waiting for a doctor to come and see her. As the mayhem increased around her, Betty's breathing had become steadily worse. All alone, unable to shout or call for help, she was simply focusing all her attention on trying to get enough air into her lungs to stay alive. When I walked in I saw the recognition on her face. She tried to tell me something but the effort was too much and instead she gently shook her head and grasped my hand.

Betty had been short of breath ever since I'd known her, but I had never seen her look this bad. Watching someone unable to breathe is horrendous. How it must feel for the poor sufferer I can't imagine and I was finding it difficult to watch Betty suffer so terribly in front of my eyes.

The department was chaotic, but Betty was sick and needed expert help. I started her on a BiPAP, a machine that helps the patient to breathe more easily, and called the doctors from intensive care. Betty was too sick to go to a ward. She needed to go to intensive care where they had all the equipment and expertise to get to grips with her breathing and possibly even put her on a ventilation machine. The specialist intensive care doctor clip-clopped into the department in her high heels. She was South African and looked impossibly young and elegant. Tall and slim, with perfect hair and make-up, she was a stark contrast to us dishevelled A&E staff wearing faded scrubs and grubby trainers. I carefully told her Betty's history and observations.

'I don't think she's really appropriate for the intensive care unit,' she said curtly after listening to my referral.

'What do you mean "not appropriate"? How sick does she have to be?'

'It's not that she's not sick; it's just that I think her outlook is poor. She has end-stage lung disease and everything points to there not being much room for improvement.'

I was fuming. 'You've barely even waved your nose in front of her and you're condemning her to death. How bloody dare you ...'

Slightly taken aback by my response, the impossibly elegant doctor looked down at me in surprise. 'I think you might have got too attached to your patient,' she retorted. 'I'll have a chat with my consultant and get back to you, but I'm fairly sure he'll back me up on this one. I think she needs palliative care rather than intensive care.'

I went back into Betty's cubicle and grabbed her hand. 'I'm having some trouble with the specialist team but I'll get you to ICU, don't worry.'

Betty shook her head and gestured for me to turn the noisy BiPAP oxygen machine off.

With the machine quiet, she mustered up all her energy to say, 'No, darling. Thank you but let me go. This really is my final curtain call.' With that she attempted a smile and held my hand. I was surprised to find a tear running down my cheek and to my annoyance realised that the intensive care doctor was right.

'Is there anyone you'd like me to call?'

Betty shook her head and now it was her turn to shed a tear.

With the noise and chaos of the busy department engulfing us, I managed to sit quietly with Betty for 10 minutes holding her hand. Our little cubicle, with the curtains drawn, was like a tiny oasis of reflection, and although Betty had her eyes closed, I'm sure she knew I was there. When I couldn't justify leaving my colleagues to face the constant onslaught any longer without my help, I gave Betty a kiss on the cheek and said goodbye. She was admitted to the respiratory ward and slipped away that night.

Smelly bum

John was absolutely convinced that his bum smelled. So much so that this was his fourth or fifth visit to see me with the same problem.

'You've got to help me, Doctor, the smell is repulsive. It's repugnant. It follows me everywhere.'

'Do you wash it regularly?'

'Yes, Doctor, of course I wash it. I scrub it every morning and evening. Nothing I do makes any difference. I'm sure everyone can smell it: the woman who sits next to me at work, people sitting behind me on the bus. I just can't go on like this any more.'

'And it's not a flatulence issue here? I mean, you don't just need to cut down on the cabbage and beans?'

John looked at me as if I was a complete idiot. 'No, Doctor! It smells all the time. Not because I fart or haven't washed. Every minute of every hour of every day I can smell it and it stinks!'

I was at a bit of a loss. I had sent samples of his poo to the lab to be tested and ordered all sorts of blood tests. I even put my finger up his behind to make sure that there wasn't some sort of anal tumour that was giving off the smell. The last time he was in I even tried a Google search of 'smelly bum', but other than getting a list of some very odd and unsavoury sites not appropriate for workplace internet browsing, I was still at a complete loss.

'So has anyone else actually ever commented on the smell?'

'No, but it's not the sort of thing that you actually ask someone is it. "Can you smell my bum?" I'm sure they can all smell it but are just being too polite to say. I've not had a girlfriend for years because I'm terrified she'd just dump me because of it and then tag a photo of me as "smelly bum" on Facebook.'

Although John had seen me on numerous occasions about this problem, on each occasion I had simply ordered another test and sent him on his way. This time I had run out of tests and really I needed to do what I should have done the first time he came in.

'John, I need to smell your bottom.'

'Excuse me?'

'If you really feel that your bum smells this bad, but only you have smelled it, you need me to smell it and tell you if this really is a problem or not.'

This is how I found myself in a scenario I never imagined I would have to face. Some of you may feel that doctors are over-paid and perhaps you're right, but how many of you reading this have a job that involves placing your nose in the close vicinity of a naked man's bottom? John was leaning over the couch with his trousers and pants around his ankles. He was holding apart his bum cheeks and as I kneeled down on the floor, I wondered how close I would actually have to place my nose to his anus to satisfactorily complete the examination. I was doing my very best to suppress my oversensitive gag reflex and feeling bitter that of all the doctors working at this practice, John had chosen to come to see me. As I got closer to John's anus, I realised I was instinctively holding my breath, so had to consciously make an effort to open my nostrils and take a big whiff.

I was prepared for the worst but to my surprise, John's bum smelled fine. It didn't smell like spring meadows or an ocean breeze, but there was certainly not the horrendous reek that he had been describing. Having never actively smelled any other man's behind, I was lacking a benchmark for comparison, but to my part relief and part annoyance, there was absolutely no reason why I needed to have my nostrils in such close proximity to his anus.

John was overjoyed when I told him his bum didn't smell. He did need some convincing and at one point seemed to be suggesting that I check again, but fortunately he did eventually take my word for it. Having managed to belatedly resolve the dilemma of the phantom smelly-bum syndrome, I had two options: I could of course simply wave John on his way having cured him of his complaint, or I could take the professional and appropriate option, which was to sit John back down and delve deeply into his inner psyche, to try to establish what previous trauma had culminated in his long-lasting and deeply disturbing delusional paranoia about his bottom.

I thought about it for a millisecond …

'Bye, John. Glad we've sorted this all out for you. All the best.'

As far as I'm concerned, smelling John's bum was already beyond the call of duty that afternoon. His 10 minutes were up and the opportunity to explore his inner psyche would have to wait for another day.

Tarig II

It had been a few months since I had last seen Tarig and failed yet again to persuade him to agree to take HIV medication. Unexpectedly, I had a request to urgently phone his wife. I didn't know Tarig's wife well as she rarely came in to see me, but I often wondered what she made of his decision to not treat his HIV. She herself had tested negative to the disease and had, on the surface at least, stuck loyally by her husband's side. She must have known that his decision not to have treatment was effectively a choice to commit suicide.

'Doctor, please come. Tarig is confused and unwell.'

As I arrived, his wife greeted me at the door.

'Doctor, please don't mention the HIV in front of the children. They don't know,' she whispered.

Tarig was in bed looking pale and unwell. He was saying some words in a language that I took to be Arabic, but his wife assured me that he was confused and making no sense. It was clear that Tarig was really sick. Once the immune system becomes very weak, numerous types of infection can take hold and I wasn't sure which one was making Tarig so unwell. Severe forms of pneumonia and meningitis are common, but regardless of which infection had taken hold, he clearly needed to go to hospital. In any other circumstances, I wouldn't have thought twice about calling an ambulance for such a severely unwell man in his 40s. With Tarig, though, we had spoken on numerous occasions about his specific wishes not to be treated for his HIV. In hindsight I wish we had put together some sort of living will or something in writing to prepare for this very situation. We hadn't, so I had to make a decision. Tarig's wife and two teenage children were in floods of tears. There was no way that I could leave him at home to die. He was now too confused and unwell to refuse hospital admission, so I went against my patient's previously expressed wishes and dialled 999.

These decisions are really tricky. If a person is actively suicidal and threatening to jump off the nearest building, they can be 'sectioned' (compulsorily detained in a psychiatric hospital) and incarcerated against their will for their own safety. Tarig's refusal to take medication to treat his HIV was equally suicidal in its nature, but he wasn't mentally unwell. He fully understood the implications of his actions and although most people would feel that this decision was wrong, there is no law against being wrong. The alternative to leaving him to die would be to lock up Tarig against his will and to hold him down and force him to take medication every day. I've seen this done in psychiatric units and it is frightening and brutal to watch. Severely mentally ill patients are only forced to take medication for a short period of time because they are so unwell that in their psychotic state they have no concept of what is real and what isn't. They don't have the ability to weigh up decisions rationally. The same couldn't be said for Tarig. He had been calm and rational during our previous conversations and well aware of the implications of the decision he was making. Right now, though, he wasn't well and as he had lost the ability to make a rational decision, I made one for him.

I worried about the ethics of that decision for some time afterwards. However, after spending some time in hospital, Tarig was discharged home and to my amazement he was voluntarily taking HIV medication. 'I had a lot of time to think in hospital and I decided that God wasn't ready for me to die just yet,' he explained.

'Good,' was all I decided to say in response. He neither thanked me nor criticised me for my decision to send him to hospital that day and so we never discussed it.

Over the previous year I had engaged Tarig in numerous theological debates and completely failed to persuade him that God didn't want him to die. Clearly it took his own near-death experience for him to come to this conclusion himself. I'm just relieved that he did.

Should we know how much
health care costs?

The NHS is running out of money. We are told this on an almost daily basis, but what you may not be aware of is that GPs like me have been told that we are now going to be the people in charge of balancing the books. One of the reasons that GPs have been given this large responsibility is that we generally run our own surgeries fairly efficiently and it would appear that, at the time of writing, the coalition feel that this effective management can be extended to the entire NHS. The truth is, I don't really know much about accountancy. My surgery runs efficiently enough, but only due to my heavy reliance on our practice manager. She steadfastly makes sure that there is enough money for everyone to get paid and that we get the best deal on our toilet roll order. I get on with trying to make the patients get better and as a business plan it works well enough.

I was against the new health legislation, but am not totally against both doctors and patients actually knowing how much things cost. Each day I sit with a metaphorical book of blank cheques of taxpayers' money and I write up prescriptions, order tests and make hospital referrals. All of these have a price and therefore cost money to the NHS and hence all of us who pay tax. Up until recently I was blissfully ignorant as to how much these all cost, but GPs are now being put in charge of the local health budgets and as a result of these changes, I am now beginning to get an idea.

Many doctors and patients are scared of thinking of health care in terms of money. The fear is that we medics will no longer see you all as real people in need of medical support, but instead as pricey leeches draining away our budgets. I would like to think I am capable of considering the financial value of what I do without it automatically having a detrimental effect on my clinical decisions.

If it were up to me, I would make up for the NHS shortfall by scrapping the recommissioning of Trident nuclear submarines – £20 billion would make our budgeting meetings considerably easier to bear. With that sort of injection of cash, the improvements we could make to patient care would be staggering. Of course, the whole point of the coalition's new health act is to make do with less money rather than more and therefore the only places we'll find any cash will be through reducing our own inefficiencies. Anyone who works within the NHS could list several ways in which we could work more efficiently. Traditionally, doctors have thought of these shortcomings in terms of wasted time for us, and poor service for patients, but now we will be encouraged to think of them from a more financial perspective.

My first job after qualifying was as a junior surgical doctor and I had a particularly frightening consultant. His ward rounds were terrifying and when he demanded a patient's blood results, I was expected to know them. If I didn't have them to hand I was on the end of a bollocking that could be heard from the other side of the hospital. My response to this was to do blood

110

tests on all my patients every day to make sure that I had every possible result to hand. Not only were my poor patients often unnecessarily stabbed with a needle each morning, but I must have personally cost the NHS a small fortune. How much? I have no idea. To this day I don't know the cost of a standard blood test, but I should, shouldn't I? I'm not suggesting that doctors shouldn't order blood tests any more, but clearly knowing the financial value alongside the clinical value of what we do is important.

One of my patients got the shock of his life recently when he discovered the actual cost of the injections he is having for his rheumatoid arthritis. He has one per week and they cost £178.75 each. That's twice his weekly rent. He wanted to know if he should add them to his house insurance, as when he has four syringes of the stuff sitting in his fridge, they are more valuable than anything else he owns. Of course I don't begrudge him these injections. I am extremely proud that the NHS provides them for him. They have allowed him to continue working and kept him off benefits. They make a massive difference to his quality of life, but I'm glad he knows their financial value as it means that he treats them with the respect they deserve. He understands how precious each vial is and ensures that they don't get smashed or accidentally thrown out with the mouldy vegetables when his fridge gets a clean.

The government is planning to send us all a breakdown of exactly what our tax is spent on. Should we be sent something similar about how much we cost in terms of our health care? I don't want anyone to be made to feel guilty about using the NHS, but how many of my patients who miss a hospital appointment realise that each failed attendance costs around £120. Or that it costs £59.48 for the asthma inhaler that keeps getting left on the bus and £244 for the ambulance needed to get to A&E after drinking to oblivion on a Saturday night. I don't advocate anything other than a free health service at the point of delivery, but just knowing the financial value of what is provided is a good thing for patients and doctors alike, isn't it?

Danni I

One of the most striking things about Danni was how unattractive she was. I couldn't quite believe that men paid money to have sex with her. This can't help but sound incredibly mean, but it really was my gut reaction when she first told me her profession. Danni was 25 years old, but so slight and slim she had the body of a 13-year-old. Her face, however, looked older than her years and was dominated by bulging dark eyes with large bags underneath and sharp protruding cheekbones. Her lips were thin and the angles of her mouth were cracked with sore-looking red lines. The medical term is angular cheilitis and I remember learning at medical school about various causes. In Danni's case the cause was basically malnutrition. The only things that went in her mouth were Coca-Cola, cigarettes, a crack pipe and her clients' penises.

I was curious to know how much she charged. I knew she spent almost every penny she earned on crack, but I wondered whether she got paid directly by her pimp in drugs, or got to walk away with a bit of cash in her pocket. I nearly asked her, but deep down I knew that I couldn't really justify this question as part of my medical consultation. She had a childlike respect for authority and if I'd asked the question she would have answered without hesitation. Much as I was tempted it wasn't fair for me to feed my voyeuristic intrigue. I also didn't want her to get the wrong idea as to why I might be asking about prices for her services.

I could tell Danni was nervous because she was incessantly putting Chapstick on her lips. Taking off the lid, twisting the bottom and smearing her lips every few seconds. I'm fairly sure she didn't even realise she was doing it and the Chapstick was probably a substitute for the cigarette with which she could normally occupy her hands.

'I'm sorry, Dr Daniels, but I'm a bit mucky down below. I think I might have picked something up again.' She looked genuinely apologetic, as if she'd really let me down.

'I thought you promised me you were always going to use protection from now on.'

'Yeah, I meant to, but it's getting harder and harder to find decent punters. The Eastern European girls have driven the prices down and I can only get work now if I go bare back. It's the recession.'

Normally it was just plumbers and carpenters who complained to me about EU labour migration and the double-dip recession. I hadn't realised it was affecting the oldest profession as well.

'But it's dangerous, Danni. You could catch HIV.'

Danni looked up at me like I had just told her off; I had rarely felt so paternal towards a patient.

'He was one of my regulars, so I thought it would be okay.'

The idea that a client who regularly used prostitutes would be less likely to have an STI seemed an odd concept but I wasn't going to take her up on it.

'He's the dad of my two kids,' she added nonchalantly.

'The dad of your two kids is still one of your clients? Do you still charge him?'

'Well, he pays the other girls so I don't see why he shouldn't pay me.'

After a few years in this job I thought nothing could surprise me, but Danni had left me absolutely speechless.

'He's not looking after your kids, is he?'

'No, they're still with the foster family. The social worker says that if I stay clean for six months I'll be allowed supervised contact.'

'That's great and how's that going? Staying clean I mean.'

Danni's hesitation said it all and we both knew she was no closer to kicking her habit.

I ended the awkward silence by asking her to get up on the couch so I could examine her. The discharge looked and smelled like gonorrhoea, but I sent off some swabs to be sure. Some of the medical advances made over the last 150 years have been incredible, but go back to Victorian Britain and you would have found a doctor like me examining prostitutes for gonorrhoea in much the same way. Medics can now look at MRI scans on their iPhones and blast away tumours with lasers, but we can't seem to stop those same old-fashioned gonorrhoea bacteria being passed to and fro in precisely the same way they always have done. In Victorian times doctors prescribed prostitutes with compulsory doses of mercury and arsenic for gonorrhoea. At least Danni had come to see me voluntarily and I could give her antibiotics rather than poison. There have been reports of antibiotic-resistant strains of gonorrhoea, but thankfully our local variety generally still responds to penicillin.

'I am sorry, Doctor,' Danni repeated.

'Don't be sorry, Danni. I just want you to look after yourself.'

'I will, I promise.'

The NHS, the envy of the world?

The NHS is the envy of the world … although apparently it's not the envy of many Polish people living in the UK. Such is their dissatisfaction with our health-care system, many of my Polish patients go home to seek medical care and two Polish doctors have set up their own private clinic in London, which is apparently thriving. I could quote data showing how good our health care outcomes are in comparison to other nations, but for most people, personal experiences outweigh any statistical evidence that I can offer.

One of my young Polish patients asked me why doctors in the NHS only prescribe paracetamol. The answer is, of course, that we don't. I prescribed him paracetamol for his slightly sore knee and explained that it would get better on its own. He told me that in Poland he would have got an X-ray and seen an orthopaedic surgeon. I also prescribed him paracetamol for his viral sore throat. In Poland his doctor would have apparently performed a chest X-ray and given antibiotics. I have prescribed him only simple painkillers for his ailments because they are benign and due to the amazing self-healing power of the human body they will get better all on their own. He is a fit 28-year-old who doesn't need extensive medical investigations for his minor health complaints, but were a privately run health clinic to be set up in our local town, I suspect he would happily part with £70 to see a non-NHS GP. I've not seen many private doctors prescribe a cheap drug like paracetamol when they can prescribe numerous more expensive ones. It would also be lucrative for a private practitioner to order as many expensive investigations as possible. These should be done quickly, as once the patient gets better, he may not be quite so willing to part with his credit card details.

Going against the grain, I do have one Polish patient who isn't quite so critical of the NHS. She is only 23 years old and has been working here as a waitress. She came to see me one afternoon with a lump on her arm. It was hard and craggy and felt like it was attached to the bone. I placed her urgently on the cancer referral pathway and within 10 days she had seen a specialist, who unfortunately agreed with my diagnosis. She had a rare aggressive bone cancer called an osteosarcoma and it needed urgent treatment. She was sent to the Royal National Orthopaedic Hospital in London where she received top-notch cancer treatment and the sort of specialist surgery that only a few places in the world can offer. She is now back at work with only a small scar on her forearm to remind her of her recent brush with death. She went back home to Warsaw last month to take her notes and scans to a Polish doctor for his opinion. He told her that the management for her condition in Poland would have been to amputate her arm above the elbow.

Those most ill tend not to be the ones who complain loudly about the NHS. A person who has been hit by a bus or is being treated for cancer tends to sing praises for the treatment they receive. The private clinics steer well clear of those who are seriously unwell as there is no money to be made from them. I can't imagine a team of private doctors offering to set up an independent A&E department. The private sector prefer to cherry pick the fortunate majority, who are basically fairly well but are often disgruntled with the NHS. The private health-care system in the USA is extremely lucrative for the same reason. They also make their huge profits by targeting their services to well people. For example, they have scared the population into believing that they all need yearly colonoscopies to screen for bowel cancer. Each colonoscopy test costs on average $1,185, while here in the UK we test poo for signs of bowel cancer instead which costs around £10. Studies suggest that both techniques have similar levels of effectiveness as a screening tool, but the American insurance companies can't make any money out of a £10 poo test. Of course, the real crime in the USA is that people with bowel cancer but no health insurance die, unable to afford a colonoscopy or the potentially life-saving treatment they need. Thank goodness for the NHS.

Much as I love the principles of the NHS, I don't live in a bubble and I would be the first to admit that it can be a bit rubbish sometimes, as can some of the people who work within it. We need to constantly root out our failings and strive to improve it from within. Sometimes this feels like an impossible task and when the NHS is on the receiving end of a constant barrage of abuse from the media, it can be tempting to look to the private sector as a way out. A private health clinic recently asked me if I'd consider leaving the NHS to become a private GP. I said no, and for two reasons. The first was that if patients are really sick, there is nothing better than our local NHS services. Secondly, I became a doctor to provide sick people with what they need, rather than offer well people what they want.

Don't look down

'Don't look down, Ben,' I was saying to myself over and over in my head. My throat was tightening and beads of sweat were forming on my forehead. No, I wasn't walking a tightrope across the Grand Canyon – it was much harder than that. I was trying to maintain eye contact with a patient and avoid looking down at her ridiculously enormous breasts.

Well into her late 40s, every other part of Julie's body was moving in a southerly direction, but somehow her breasts were defying Newton's laws and appeared perfectly suspended by an invisible force that was maintaining them at an exact right angle to her body. I was rather hoping that Julie was completely unaware of the tricky battle going on in my head, but I suspect not. She was wearing a particularly skimpy top given the cold spell of weather we'd been having and just when I seemed to be successfully maintaining uninterrupted eye contact, she would push her chest out and wriggle in her seat, throwing me completely off my game.

I had met Julie once or twice before, but had no previous recollection of her breasts. I would like to point out that I don't generally remember my patients on the basis of their bra size, but such was the oddity of the bosoms that I was trying desperately to ignore that I couldn't believe they would have previously passed me by unnoticed. I had watched enough episodes of *Celebrity Big Brother* to be able to at least hazard a guess that they were fake, but such was my desperation not to be caught staring that I couldn't be 100 per cent sure that they were in fact due to prosthetics rather than genetics.

After the normal small talk about the weather, Julie told me why she was there.

'I just need another sick note, Doctor.'

Scanning through her medical notes, I could see that Julie only ever really attended the surgery for sick notes. Every six months or so she would see a doctor and be signed off work for depression. She had always declined counselling or antidepressants, but when on her last visit I'd asked her to fill in a depression questionnaire, she scored maximum points and so the sick note was extended. Surely this time I couldn't sign her off work quite so readily. She had almost certainly had a boob job since her last visit and this was throwing me into an ethics minefield. Can you really be too depressed to work yet voluntarily endure the pain and stress of major cosmetic surgery? What about the money? Are you allowed to claim benefits if you have a spare £6,000 for a new set of breasts? Most importantly for me, how was I going to broach this sensitive subject? Such was my inert sense of awkwardness, I could barely bring myself to even glance at Julie's breasts, let alone declare them as a topic of conversation. Imagine the embarrassment I would face if I cited her false breasts as evidence that she couldn't be depressed and they turned out to be real! I decided I would have to approach the subject from a different angle.

'So, how is your depression at the moment, Julie?'

'Actually, not that bad, Doctor. I'm feeling happier than I have done for a long time.'

Great, I thought to myself. No sick note for you, and I wouldn't have to mention the two white elephants in the room. This was turning out to be considerably less stressful than I had feared.

'I was depressed before, so my Gary bought me these new boobs for my birthday and it's worked a treat. My Gary always knows how to cheer me up and they've put a big smile on his face too! What do you reckon of them?' Julie asked, proudly pushing her chest in my direction.

'Well, erm … I hadn't really erm … noticed …'

'Oh get away, Dr Daniels, you've barely taken your eyes off them since I walked through the door,' she said, smiling broadly.

I was now staring at my computer screen intently pretending to be checking something important, while secretly wishing the ground would swallow me whole.

'Well … erm Julie, so … erm … getting back to the reason for your visit here today. Surely you don't really need a sick note any more now that you're no longer depressed?'

'Thing is, Doctor, I am much happier now, but my Gary's a cheeky little rascal and he ordered a cup size or two too big. Let me tell you these things weigh an absolute ton and my back is bloody killing me. So if you could just cross out depression on the sick note and replace it with back pain that would be grand.'

Mrs Patrick

Mrs Patrick was my nemesis. As already mentioned, she was the very first patient I had seen at this surgery and I can still remember her venomous distrust in me the first time we met. Her misgivings about me had not diminished, but nor had they prevented her from visiting me at least once per week for the past nine months. Such was the frequency of her visits that some days I spent considerably more time with her than I did my own wife.

'Just a few problems today, Doctor,' she uttered as she pulled out a lengthy list of her ailments neatly jotted in blue biro on a scrap of paper.

The production of a 'list' always causes my heart to sink a little, but when the list belonged to Mrs Patrick, I usually completely lost the will to live. It was a Thursday morning and I had last seen Mrs Patrick on the preceding Monday afternoon. How could she have developed a brand new list of medical ailments in less than 72 hours?

'Well, first of all I'm getting terrible headaches.'

Mrs Patrick declared this complaint as if it was the first time it had ever been mentioned to a doctor. She had in fact been suffering from headaches since before I was born. It was first documented in her notes in 1974 and I wondered just how many GPs, neurologists and pain specialists had heard about her headaches over the past 40 years. As technology developed so did Mrs Patrick's headache investigation. When the CT scanner was invented, her doctor referred her for a CT scan. When the MRI scanner was devised, she was diligently sent for an MRI scan. I could just picture her disappointment as each new ground-breaking investigation reported her brain as being completely normal. Over the last four decades numerous new headache medications had come onto the market. A succession of doctors had endeavoured to embrace these latest pharmacological discoveries for her benefit, but without exception each pioneering medication had offered no relief. Continuing this trend, my latest desperate attempt at curing her headaches had fared no better: 'Those tablets you gave me made my headaches about a million times worse,' she snarled at me as if I had prescribed them in a deliberate attempt to cause her distress.

On Monday, Mrs Patrick had told me that her headaches were 11 out of 10 on a pain scale, but nonetheless I feebly apologised for somehow causing them to increase by one-million-fold.

Now, I don't wish to sound unsympathetic. Headaches are horrible. Millions suffer from them, including myself, and they cause untold misery. In fact, a great many of my patients have chronic long-standing health complaints that we muddle through together and I would like to think that I mostly offer empathy and support. My issue with Mrs Patrick is that she seems to actually revel in her ill health. Despite her clear disdain for me and the majority of the medical profession, she seems almost addicted to spending an enormous amount of her free time sitting in front of me and numerous hospital specialists recounting her torment. My computer told me that it was her 31st consultation with me in the nine months since I had arrived at the surgery. During this time, both Mrs Patrick and I would fervently agree that we had made absolutely no advancement whatsoever in resolving her headaches or any other of her ever-increasing catalogue of ailments. Despite my failure to provide her even the smallest morsel of symptom relief, here she was, sat before me, yet again reciting the persistent misery of her symptoms.

This particular morning's consultation followed the normal routine and once she had offloaded the wretchedness of her headaches, we moved on to the dizzy spells, persistent nausea, sneezing fits and funny turns. Without fail, each effort I made to suggest a possible solution was met with disdain and rejection until I was left slumped in my chair simply waiting for the torture to end. After 30 minutes, I sensed that Mrs Patrick was tiring and the consultation was finally reaching its closing stages. Unfortunately, any relief I might get from her eventual departure was tarnished by the knowledge that it would only be a few days until she would be back in to see me and the whole painful process would be repeated all over again.

'Mrs Patrick, I've got an idea,' I almost shouted, interrupting her mid-flow in her fifth complaint of the session.

Mrs Patrick looked at me suspiciously.

'Would you agree that we've tried lots and lots of things to try to resolve your headaches, dizzy spells, nausea, sneezing and funny turns?'

'Well, yes, tried a lot, but they've all been bloody useless, haven't they?'

'Exactly!' I declared triumphantly, as if this was in fact something to be pleased about.

'So, I've got a new plan.' I paused for effect. 'We're going to stop all your medications and we're not going to prescribe any new ones or refer you to any specialists.'

'Eh?' Mrs Patrick looked at me as if I had completely lost the plot.

'Well, we've failed, haven't we? I mean, you've seen me 31 times in the last nine months and before me there was Dr Bailey and many other doctors before him.'

'Well, yes, but you can't just stop my pills?'

'Sometimes we just have to accept as doctors that some medical problems are beyond our realm of knowledge. It is important to know when to throw up our hands and admit defeat. You said yourself that not a single one of your tablets makes even the first bit of difference to any of your symptoms, so let's stop them all.'

'But not the painkillers?'

'Yep, all those painkillers that don't stop your pain. We're going to stop all of those.'

'But not the creams and the nasal sprays?'

'The creams that don't clear up your invisible rash and the nasal sprays that don't do a thing for your snuffly nose. We're going to stop those too.'

'So, can't I come and see you any more?'

'Of course you can, but we're just going to agree that medical science will never cure you of your symptoms, so instead we're going to talk about other things that might help.'

'Er, like what?' Mrs Patrick asked, looking visibly nervous.

'Have you ever had a dog?'

'A dog?'

'Or joined a choir?'

'Are you okay, Dr Daniels?'

'Yes, I really am,' I said, meaning it.

'Getting a dog and joining a choir?'

'Yes, or whatever else inspires you to smile and enjoy yourself! You can still come and see me and we'll talk about all the other things you're going to do in your life rather than take medicines and go to hospital appointments.'

'But we're not going to talk about my headaches?'

'Exactly!'

'Or my dizzy spells, or sneezing, or nausea, or funny turns?'

'That's right.'

'A dog and a choir?' Mrs Patrick repeated to herself quietly as she left the room.

This was going to go one of two ways. I was either going to make a massive breakthrough and after 40 years finally free Mrs Patrick and the medical profession from much of her torment. Or I was going to end up being struck off the medical register for suggesting singing and dog walking as a cure for some sort of rare medical syndrome that Mrs Patrick's next doctor was going to cleverly diagnose.

Danni II

'You've gotta sort this out, Doc. I can't get no business.'

Danni was pointing to an unpleasant looking cold sore on her upper lip. It had become infected and scabby lesions were spreading up to her nose and cheek.

As a sex worker, the infection on her face meant that she couldn't get any clients and so couldn't earn any money. If she had been a teacher with a hoarse voice or a carpet fitter with bad knees I could have given her a sick note so that she could get sick pay, but in her line of work there wasn't that sort of safety net.

'I can't even hide it with make-up.'

Danni had been my patient for some time and I knew her biggest concern about not working would be that she couldn't afford to buy herself any heroin or crack.

'How are you buying your gear if you can't work?'

'I've had to go to the clinic and get some methadone.'

I had once thought that methadone was used to wean people off opiates, but my patients who are drug users mostly just use it to keep them going if they can't get hold of any heroin. Some of them stay on methadone for years and years, constantly putting off the gradual reduction of the dose that is supposed to wean them off drug dependency for good.

'Are you on benefits?' I ask.

'No, most of the girls are on benefits, but I don't think it's right getting money from the government when I'm earning.'

I was surprised by Danni's moral stance. It seemed odd when someone who was living so far outside of what might be considered 'morally normal' was taking a principled stand about claiming benefits. I doubt she ever paid tax on her earnings, but even so her sense of ethical responsibility was admirable.

Danni only ever came in to see me for emergency appointments. I could often help with the superficial problems, such as dealing with an abscess from where she had injected heroin, or treating a sexually transmitted infection, as I had last time she had been in. Frustratingly, I could never get to the real root of her problems, which was depression and addiction.

It didn't take long to prescribe Danni some antibiotics for the infection on her face, but she didn't seem to want to leave. 'While I'm here, Doctor, I wondered if I could just talk to you about something else?'

'Well, not really, Danni. I fitted you in for an emergency appointment and I'm already running late. The waiting room is heaving.'

'Oh yeah, of course, Doctor, I'm sorry. I don't wanna waste your time.'

I felt instantly guilty for cutting Danni short. It was true that I was running late and the waiting room was full, but the other reason I was keen for Danni to leave was that she always made me feel so bloody useless. Her life was so complex and chaotic that I never felt able to even scratch the surface of her problems. I couldn't cure the general sense of misery that ran at the heart of her day-to-day existence. There was nothing I could do to make her life anything close to resembling happy, so I really just wanted her to leave my room so that someone whom I could actually help might come in.

I once heard someone say that life was like treading water in a swimming pool of raw sewage and that the job of a GP is to direct people to the shallow end. Danni was drowning in the deep end and if I couldn't dive in and drag her out, the least I could do was offer her a sympathetic ear while she flailed around in the faeces.

'Sorry, Danni, what were you going to ask me?'

'Well, it's just that I've got no money, and until my face gets better I can't earn anything and well … I'm just really hungry.'

A tide of genuine shame washed over me. Danni was suffering from that such basic but unpleasant of human sensations – hunger. And oddly enough that was one of her few problems I could help with. There wasn't a huge amount of food in the building, but I found an apple, four packets of spicy tomato and vegetable cup-a-soup and half a packet of chocolate digestives. I shoved them all into a carrier bag and pressed it into Danni's hand. It didn't constitute the most appetising or nutritious of suppers, but it was likely to contain more calories than she had eaten in days. I did at one point consider giving her a tenner so she could buy herself a hot dinner, but giving cash to patients is crossing a boundary too far, and besides, however hungry she was, the money would have been spent on drugs rather than food.

Danni clearly felt a bit awkward accepting my gift but hunger soon took precedence over pride and she gratefully shoved the food parcel into her handbag.

'You really didn't have to do that, Doctor. I could have nicked myself something from Sainsbury's.'

'It's no bother, Danni. The last thing you need is to get caught shoplifting again.'

Danni gave me a smile and left. She looked genuinely touched by what she perceived to be a great act of kindness. The reality was that I was relieved to be able to do something simple, practical and worthwhile rather than squirm in my chair feeling completely useless in the way I normally did. Danni was still drowning in the swimming pool of excrement, but at least she could nourish herself with a few chocolate digestives chucked at her from the side.

Unnoticed

Sue, our receptionist, was always the first to know everything about everyone in our surgery, so it was no surprise that she was the one to tell us that Mr Brading had died. 'Oh yeah, Mr Brading. Not seen him for a while,' was my comment when she first told me the news.

'Well, that's not surprising. His neighbours reported a smell coming from his flat. When the police broke in they found him half decayed with an army of maggots having taken up residence. There was unopened post from over four months ago.'

I could actually remember Robert Brading very well. He was a big chap who smoked and drank too much. He came in fairly often and he liked to talk about his time doing military service and his love for motorbikes. I mostly lectured him on stopping smoking and improving his diet. At his last appointment with me I organised a blood test and asked him to come back and see me the following week. He made the appointment, but didn't turn up. That was four months ago and was probably the week he died. How could no one on the planet have noticed he was gone for all that time?

Perhaps saddest of all is the fact that last month was his 70th birthday. Rather than celebrating with family and friends, he had been lying decaying in his armchair, the day passing by unnoticed. I hope that the pile of unopened mail on his doormat included at least one or two birthday cards.

I, of course, am equally guilty of being oblivious to Mr Brading's sudden demise. I had sat at this desk seeing patient after patient with ailment after ailment. I was focused on those in front of me rather than wondering why a patient had suddenly stopped visiting me. Scrolling through the notes of our previous consultations, I see that we had seen each other numerous times in the few months before his death. Never once did I ask about family or friends or find out who he was as a person. All that I appeared to have offered him was a series of lectures on improving his lifestyle: Give up smoking! Lose weight! Eat less salt! A bombardment of instructions guided by my computer flashing up a succession of targets that Mr Brading was failing to meet. He had wanted to talk to me about motorbikes and his days in the army but I hadn't had time for that.

I went home that night trying to imagine how anyone could live for 70 years and then die unnoticed. I hadn't known Mr Brading personally, but surely there must have been times in his life when he had friends and family. Was there a moment that he knew he was dying and if so, did he regret how isolated he had become? Bronnie Ware, an Australian palliative care nurse, wrote a fascinating essay listing the biggest regrets of the dying. She consistently observed that one of the biggest regrets of those soon to depart was losing touch with old friends. I spent the evening phoning a couple of old university friends who I hadn't seen for far too long. A reunion was organised and after some happy hours of catching up with old chums, I quietly toasted Mr Brading for reminding me of life's priorities.

Man flu

Man flu can be a cruel, cruel illness. My empathy levels for grown men coming to see me with a sore throat and the sniffles might be low, but when I myself am afflicted with this unforgiving disease, I crumble into a ball of snuffling self-pity and will complain endlessly to anyone who has the misfortune of my company.

On this particular Friday afternoon my captive audience was Vanessa, my medical student; she had been sitting in with me for three weeks. I like to try to convince myself that the medical students see me as a young, trendy doctor barely much older than themselves. I ask them what music they listen to and make sure they call me Ben rather than Dr Daniels. As each year goes by I find this an increasingly difficult undertaking to pull off. Bright eyed and enthusiastic, Vanessa seemed to take an interest in absolutely everything and everyone. Not once had I witnessed her display even the slightest hint of cynicism and it was perhaps this overwhelming positivity, even more than her youthful looks, that made me feel so very much older than her.

'I never get colds,' Vanessa gushed brightly as I explained my ill health.

Good for you, Vanessa, I thought as I wallowed further in the misery wreaked by the combination of afternoon surgery and my terrible man-flu symptoms. The constant stream of patients was exhausting but just about manageable and although Vanessa's incessant enthusiasm could be grating, her high energy levels were keeping me awake.

Before surgery started, I had eaten three cloves of raw garlic in a vain attempt to ward off my snuffles. I'm not sure there is any scientific evidence that raw garlic cures a cold, but anecdotally at least my pungent breath seemed to be helping prevent patients from overstaying their welcome.

Just when I thought the end of surgery was in sight, I spotted that a certain Mrs Patrick had been added to the end of my consultation list. If I'm honest, my master plan to wean her off her constant visits by encouraging non-medical interventions had failed. With some delight she informed me that getting a dog was out due to the terrible dog hair allergy that she was bound to develop, and she couldn't join a choir because the light in the hall where they rehearse might trigger off her photosensitivity reaction. Instead, she came to visit me so she could offload her ailments in the normal fashion. I would nod and listen sympathetically, but in recent weeks I had prided myself at being able to stand strong and bravely bat away her inappropriate requests for unhelpful medication and unsuitable referrals.

As she walked into my room, her first words were a damning complaint about our appointments system. Normally I would counter this by pointing out that she had in fact managed to get an appointment with me the very afternoon she called, despite having not a single ailment that could be considered even the slightest bit urgent. Instead, in my viral induced misery, I simply conceded an apology hoping to move the consultation along.

Surrendering this morsel to Mrs Patrick was a catastrophic error. Spotting I was ill, she smelled my weakness and like a shark with the taste of blood she went in for the kill.

By the end of the consultation, Mrs Patrick had managed to glean from me two inappropriate referrals, some expensive medication she didn't need and a course of antibiotics, even though she didn't have the slightest hint of an infection. I simply did not have the energy to say no to her list of extensive demands and once I had said yes once, my resolve and spirit collapsed in a broken heap. As the appointment broke the 30-minute mark, I even resorted to breathing heavily in her direction, but even with my pungent garlic halitosis I was powerless to stop her. Such was the scale of her momentum, I think even a stake through the heart would have failed to bring the consultation to an end. When she did finally get up out of her chair, I could sense her indulgently wallowing in her splendid triumph. On her way out she briefly turned around and I think I may have seen the slightest upturn of the corners of her mouth. It might have just been a twitch, but if I'm not mistaken I was quite possibly, for the first time ever, witnessing her smile.

Slumped, exhausted and broken, I glanced up at Vanessa who looked at me with what I took to be pity in her eyes. I could imagine her wondering what had become of me that I could be so thoroughly physically and emotionally broken by a middle-aged woman with a few health phobias and a pathological addiction to coming to the surgery.

'Don't worry,' I offered meekly. 'She may have won this battle, but I'll win through at the end. This is like the end of *The Empire Strikes Back* when the Jedis are all but beaten, but when I'm well again next week I'll fight back *Return of the Jedi* style.'

Vanessa gave me a very puzzled look.

'The first "Star Wars" films,' I said, surprised that this should need an explanation.

'Oh yes, I think I've heard of them. My dad probably likes them.'

Medical students

As I'd been supervising medical students like Vanessa for a little while, the local medical school asked me to be on the interview panel to help select the next year's first-year student doctors. It was a Thursday morning in late November and there was a steady stream of nervous but enthusiastic teenagers with sweaty palms and bitten nails waiting to be interviewed by a panel of three doctors, of which I was one.

These prospective medical students had already passed a stringent shortlisting process, which involved having high academic grades and passing an aptitude test. They had all written enthusiastic personal statements and had glowing references. Now it was the turn of we three doctors to make the final decision as to whether they were good enough to one day become doctors.

This is a pretty tough call to make based on spending 15 minutes or so with a nervous 17-year-old and although there is a subjective element to the decision-making process, we had set questions and a marking scheme in order to try to make everything as fair as possible. Medicine was once an extremely male-dominated profession, but now 70 per cent of students at our local medical school are female. This is fairly common throughout the country and it will be fascinating to see how the dynamics of medicine change over the next decade or so as the profession becomes increasingly female dominated.

Until I started interviewing, I couldn't work out why so many more young women were being selected over men, but as I saw more and more applicants, the reason became increasingly obvious. The girls were just so much better than the boys in the interviews. They were articulate and enthusiastic with a range of interests and could conduct themselves really well. With the odd exception, the boys couldn't. Such was the contrast that I was amazed that the percentage of male students getting in was as high as 30 per cent.

My two fellow interviewers were both female doctors and seemed undeterred by the huge mismatch in how the genders were performing. As we accepted more and more girls and rejected more and more boys I felt sure that at least one boy would do well and get offered a place. The next lad to walk in instantly reminded me of myself at his age. His shiny Marks & Spencer suit was as ill-fitting and unfashionable as the one I'd worn at my medical school interview. He was skinny and awkward and just looked so much younger and less worldly than the girls we had seen before him. His references and predicted grades were excellent and I was determined I was going to do my best to give him a really good shot. Unfortunately, despite being thoroughly likeable, he was stumbling through the questions and was scoring as badly as the other boys.

We were halfway through the interview. The next set question was to ask what he had achieved during that summer. The marking scheme gave points for voluntary work and anything that indicated a breadth of extra-curricular interests. The last girl who'd been in had told us about her charity work at a local hospice and how she had passed her grade-eight violin exam with distinction; the girl before told us of the fantastic sense of achievement she had felt on completion of her Duke of Edinburgh gold award. The young lad sitting in front of us looked completely flummoxed by the question and as far as I was concerned, rightly so. When I was 17, I spent the entirety of my summer holidays playing *Tomb Raider* on my PlayStation, getting stoned and masturbating. Charity work and music exams had been the last thing on my mind. If I could state my greatest achievements of that summer it was learning to skin up and having a moderately successful fumble in the dark with a girl I met at a music festival. By the uncomfortable dithering from the young lad in front of us, I got the impression that his summer had been equally unproductive.

'Did you go away anywhere, perhaps?' I prompted in an attempt to end the awkward silence.

'Oh yes, I went to Glastonbury with my mates.'

'Great, did you have a good time?'

'Yeah, it was the best,' he said, breaking into a big smile.

And with that I scored him maximum points on my marking sheet. As far as I was concerned, there was no reason why spending a summer practising the violin or orienteering on Dartmoor would make anyone a better doctor than going to a music festival.

After that he relaxed a bit, and as the interview went on he showed himself to be charming, intelligent and equipped with the kind of qualities we were looking for. Even my fellow interviewers were won over and we decided to offer him a place.

Taking benefits away from addicts

Crackhead Kenny had come back to see me. He bashfully apologised for storming out on me last time he was in; I told him that I accepted his apology, and I meant it. There's no room in this job for holding grudges and I was pleased that Kenny had decided to stick with me as his GP rather than move to another practice in an attempt to find a doctor who would prescribe him what I had refused.

Kenny was here to ask me for a sick note and it was a timely request as that very morning it had been reported that the government was threatening to stop heroin addicts from being able to claim incapacity benefit. About a hundred of my patients are heroin users and they are all signed off work. The government spokesman pointed out that it was unfair that hardworking taxpayers were paying for the addictions of others. This may well be true, but is an attempt to force heroin users such as Kenny into gainful employment really a viable option?

We recently advertised for an admin assistant at our surgery. It is a low paid, unskilled, part-time position that requires no previous experience and no great physical exertion. Such is the nature of the times, we had more than 60 applicants, most of whom were greatly overqualified for the post. None of the applicants were intravenous heroin users, but if any were we wouldn't have shortlisted them. If we wouldn't consider employing a heroin user, who does the government think will? With the exception of the odd ailing rock star, I am yet to hear of a gainfully employed injecting heroin addict.

Heroin is an awful, all-consuming drug that destroys the personality of the person behind the habit. The next fix becomes more important to the user than food, shelter and, most sad of all, the people who care about them most. It is not a lifestyle that can easily coexist with a nine-to-five job. As Kenny sits in front of me, I don't even consider not signing his sick note. There is no way in the world that he could hold down a job in his current state. The government is very welcome to switch Kenny and addicts like him from incapacity benefit to jobseeker's allowance, but it would simply be an expensive and time-consuming PR exercise.

If the government chooses to take it one step further and remove all drug users' benefits, the result would be an almighty hurrah from some, but it would simply mean a large number of the most vulnerable members of our society being made homeless and pushed further into crime, prostitution and begging as they looked for alternative ways to feed their habits. The extra burden placed on the criminal justice system would almost certainly end up costing far more than the relatively meagre hand-outs that heroin users currently receive in the form of incapacity benefit. It is much too simplistic to think that if we took Kenny's benefits away from him, he would be forced to stop taking drugs, find a job and instantly become a more positive and worthwhile contributor to society.

Our local drug and rehab services are very good, but although most of my patients who use heroin are actively enrolled within substance misuse services, very few will successfully turn their lives around. Treating heroin addicts punitively with prison sentences doesn't seem to work either, so it would appear to me better to try to work out why people fall into heroin addiction in the first place. Most of us experiment with drugs to some level or another in our youth, but even during my own sustained and enthusiastic period of adolescent experimentation, I never got anywhere near a place where injecting a syringe full of heroin into my arm jumped out as being a good idea.

Kenny had a 10-minute appointment with me that day and it took less than one minute to fill in a sick note. I decided that it might be an opportunity to ask him how he became an addict. The story Kenny told me was a familiar one. As with many of my patients who use heroin, he seemed to take those extra few steps into harder drugs and full-scale addiction after a fairly miserable start in life. Heroin is often an escape from the grim realities of life, and among my patients child abuse and growing up in care seem to pop up time and time again as the most damaging experiences addicts are trying to escape from.

As a doctor, I try not to get carried away with the emotion and morality of what I see because it interferes with the practical aspects of the job. Many of my patients have self-inflicted injuries and illnesses and whether they are due to heroin, alcohol, smoking or falling off ponies, offering my indignation benefits no one. In my eyes politicians have no option but to take the same approach. I am dealing with addiction on an individual basis while they have to consider it on a more national scale, but ultimately the realities are the same.

Heroin dependence exists and is hugely detrimental to everyone. Vitriolic sound bites about the cost to taxpayers might make favourable headlines in the right-wing media, but they don't make the problem go away. There will always be some people who fall prey to heroin. Whether we view this as the fault of society or the individual is meaningless. As far as I'm concerned, the real issue is trying to prevent vulnerable people like Kenny from plunging into addiction in the first place rather than seeking to blame them once they have.

Stuck in the middle

It was rare to see Tilly with both of her parents. They had split up the previous year and, although they were still being forced to live together due to the negative equity on their house, the break-up was less than amicable.

Tilly was sitting between them and she didn't look well. She was thin and pale, and her parents were clearly sufficiently worried to try to put their differences aside for long enough to come together to see me.

'Well, Dr Daniels, Tilly's not been well since he took her camping that time. I told him not to take her but he didn't take any notice.'

'Well that's nonsense, Dr Daniels – it was nothing to do with the camping. If her mum didn't let her eat so much junk food she might look a little healthier.'

'Hold on,' I interrupted. 'Can I just ask what symptoms Tilly actually has?'

'She's tired all of the time, Doctor, and she just wants to sit on the sofa and drink orange squash.'

Tilly didn't look like the lively six-year-old child I had once known.

'Any family history of anything?' I asked

'Drinking on his side,' Tilly's mum jumped in, pointing an accusatory finger at Tilly's dad. 'Practically all of them are pickled by the time they reach 40.' She started miming a swaying drunk downing a bottle of wine added with her own 'glug glug' noises

'Well at least my family have a bit of fun once in a while. The only thing that runs in your family is misery and bitterness. If you cut your mum open she'd bleed lemon juice she's so sour—'

'How about diabetes?' I interrupted

They both looked at me with concern.

'Does diabetes run in either of your families?'

For the first time Tilly's mum and dad actually looked at each other. 'No,' they both said shaking their heads in unison.

I'd just tested Tilly's urine and it was full of glucose.

'I think Tilly might have diabetes, which is why she's been feeling so unwell.'

I went through the diagnosis of diabetes with Tilly and her parents. It was scraping the surface really as there was so much new information for them to take in. I couldn't really begin to tell them everything they needed to know, but perhaps for the first time in a while they were a family again, and Tilly's mum and dad were able to put their differences aside in their shared love for their daughter.

Danni III

This time Danni had been beaten up. It wasn't the first time this had happened, but today she seemed really shaken up by it.

'I actually thought he was going to kill me, Dr Daniels. He had his hands around my neck and was throttling me like this.' She mimed herself being strangled and I could see in her face how terrified she must have been.

'Did you speak to the police?'

'Well, I gave a statement, but they didn't seem that bothered. He wasn't a regular and I was so off my tits at the time I couldn't really remember what he looked like to give a decent description.'

'Why did he attack you?'

'He paid for one thing and then wanted something extra thrown in for free. Got pissed off when I said no. Thing is, Dr Daniels, it doesn't really have to be much of an excuse for some of these blokes. I see how they look at me, as if I'm not really human. The things they say can hurt even more than the punches sometimes.'

'Well, I'll document the injuries in case it does go to court.'

'Okay, Doctor, but that's not actually why I'm here.'

'Oh?'

151

'Well, this last beating really scared me. I genuinely thought that was it. As he was strangling me all I could think about was my kids.'

Danni paused for a bit and then looked me in the eye.

'That moment was rock bottom for me and when I realised I wasn't going to die, I thought, right, Danni, you've got a second chance here. A real chance to prove everyone wrong and show that you can get your life back on track.'

'Fantastic, Danni! I'm really pleased you're making a positive out of this.'

'That's where you come in, Doctor. You've always been kind to me and I need you to help me get my kids back.'

'I'm not sure it's that simple, Danni. It's not me who makes that sort of decision.'

'I know it won't be easy, Doctor. The social workers never listen to me, but they'll listen to you. If you can tell them that I'm coming off the game and off the smack then we can stop them putting my kids up for adoption.'

I had never met Danni's children, but I had read her notes. They had been with her for a few years before being taken into care and from what I could gather being taken away from Danni was the best thing that had ever happened to them. They were thriving with a new foster family who were hoping to adopt them. They were settled in a new school and flourishing in an environment of security and stability that Danni could never offer them.

'To be fair, Danni, how many times have you promised that you're coming off the drugs before? You can see why the social workers might be dubious.'

'It's different this time. I love those kids. They're mine. They had no right to take them away. Why won't anyone believe me when I tell them that I love them?'

'But it's not enough just to love them, Danni.'

Danni was silent and I regretted my words.

'So you think I'm a shit mum as well?'

'It's not that, I know you love your children, but kids need more than just to be loved. They need to grow up feeling safe and secure. They need routine and adults they can always rely on. I'm not saying that you won't be able to offer them that one day, but I'm not sure you could right now.'

Danni looked really hurt. Filling up with tears she looked at me with venom.

'I thought you were different, Dr Daniels, but you're just like them. Judging me and making decisions about my life you've got no right to make.'

With that Danni was gone.

Danni was my patient and my duty of care was with her, but I couldn't support her trying to take her children back. How I could I write a letter suggesting that they should leave their settled and happy life and be thrown back into the chaos that was Danni's? Those children had a golden opportunity to break free from the cycle of misery that had engulfed Danni and I couldn't endanger that. Maybe Danni could break free too. Maybe this time was different and she would turn her life around. Perhaps I'd got things completely wrong and Danni could become a fantastic mother? It was a risk I was going to have to take and although Danni feels let down by me right now, I hope that someday she'll agree it was the right decision.

Funny X-ray

It was another chaotic morning in A&E and my first patient was being wheeled into the department on a specially reinforced trolley. Like other 999 services, our local paramedics had invested in some reinforced equipment in order to cater for the ever-increasing size and weight of the local population. The woman being wheeled in was huge, and we needed to transfer her from the special strong-and-wide trolley to a strong-and-wide hospital bed.

The paramedics told me that the woman had collapsed at home, and by the exhausted looks on their faces I could imagine it had been quite an effort to get her up off the floor. How they managed it I don't know, but they certainly deserved the cup of tea that was waiting for them in the staff room. There wasn't much more the paramedic crew could tell me about their patient, so I tried to ask her a few questions. Unfortunately she was confused and drowsy and only mumbled a few nonsensical remarks, so I soon gave up.

There are numerous reasons why a patient might be admitted confused and if there is no background history to help point us in the right direction, the obvious next step is to examine the patient. Sometimes examination findings alone can give us all the clues we need, but when a patient is as large as the lady in front of me was, most of the clues potentially gained from the physical examination are hidden under layers of fat. I tried to listen to her lungs, but as I endeavoured to find somewhere on her back to lay my stethoscope, I was met with so many rolls of fat that it was tricky to find a flat surface on which to place it. I tried in vain to listen to lung sounds, but the lungs were separated from my stethoscope by so many inches of fatty tissue that the sound couldn't be transmitted and I heard nothing. Examining the abdomen was no easier. As I pressed my hand on to her tummy, I knew that there was no way that I would be able to glean any useful information about the organs buried deep below. I could just about feel a pulse in her wrist and so I knew she had a heartbeat but unfortunately, again, I couldn't hear it. The ECG machine, blood pressure monitor and oxygen probe were struggling as much as I was, and after 10 minutes I realised that I was absolutely none the wiser as to why this lady was unwell.

Thank goodness for the humble chest X-ray. X-rays show the air in the lungs as black and the bones as white. Fat, even a thick layer of it, can be seen through if the clever radiographer cranks up the exposure of the film. I was depending on the chest X-ray to show me a reasonable picture of her lungs to help work out what might be going on. The portable chest X-ray was done and the picture soon showed up on the computer monitor. To my relief, the image was reasonably clear and I could see the white fuzzing of infection in the lower part of her right lung that was probably causing her problems. Oddly though, the infection wasn't the only thing that I could see. There was some sort of electrical device implanted on the left side of her chest wall. I was used to seeing pacemakers on a chest X-ray film. These are implanted under the skin on the chest; the wires from them travel to the heart and give off electrical pulses to help prevent it beating too slowly. This didn't look like a pacemaker though, because I couldn't see any wires travelling from the machine to the heart.

I called over one of the other doctors to have a look and soon there was a small collection of us crowding round the monitor trying to work out what the device was. I thought it might be an implantable defibrillator but one of the other doctors pointed out that these have visible wires too. The cardiology registrar, who was also staring in confusion, had heard about a wireless pacemaker being developed in America and wondered if this was a version. As the number of doctors surrounding the monitor grew, the debate on the identity of the mystery device intensified. During a rare moment of quiet, a voice from the back of the crowd piped up, 'It looks like a Nokia 1101.'

Everyone turned round to look at the baby-faced medical student at the back.

'Nokia don't make pacemakers,' the cardiologist snapped impatiently before returning to his debate with the emergency medicine consultant.

'No, the Nokia 1101 is a mobile phone. I used to have one and it looks identical.'

There was a moment of silence before the cardiologist continued to shout down the student for even considering that a mobile phone could be implanted inside her chest. I went back to see the patient. With a bit of help from one of the nurses I leaned her forward and pulled apart a large roll of fat on the left side of her back. I pushed my hand in and felt what I was searching for. The Nokia 1101 needed a bit of a tug, but it soon came free and I returned to the collection of doctors around the monitor to show them my catch. The medical student quite rightly enjoyed his moment of triumph while the cardiologist left quietly, shoulders slumped.

The coroner

It was 8:15 on a Wednesday morning and I had just arrived at work. I had barely taken off my coat when the receptionist put a call through to me.

'Morning, Dr Daniels, it's the coroner's office here.'

A wave of anxiety washed over me. The coroner only calls when someone has died and usually when that death is unexpected.

'Barry Dawkins. Know him? Date of birth 22 April 1963. He was found dead at home last night by his wife.'

The name rang a bell but I really couldn't picture him. Having been born in the year 1963 made him only just 50. Why had he died? That's much too young.

My slow NHS computer was taking a lifetime to boot up. I was repeating the name Barry Dawkins over and over in my mind. Why couldn't I picture him? Who was he? Had I missed something? Of course, with more than 6,000 patients registered at our surgery, one or two tend to fall off their perch every month or so, but normally these are patients who are expected to die and the coroner doesn't get involved.

The coroner's office deals with deaths that are violent or unexplained. They often call for a post-mortem and sometimes order an inquest to clarify the details surrounding the death. A coroner's inquest can be a scary place for doctors. They are not a criminal court and so can't attribute criminal negligence, but they often still involve a doctor standing up under oath and trying to justify why they did or did not do something with regard to a patient's care.

When I finally got Barry Dawkins' notes up, I scrolled through in a slight panic wondering if I might have missed something. He'd been in a few times recently for a review of his blood pressure and diabetes, but that was about it. My biggest fear was that he had presented with symptoms that I had dismissed, which he had then gone on to die from. Could he have had a burst aorta that I'd dismissed as simple back pain, or a bleed on the brain that I'd thought was a migraine? I was mightily relieved to see that no such mistake had been made, but a pang of guilt washed over me as I realised that selfish self-preservation was all I'd been able to think about upon hearing of this man's untimely death.

The coroner disrupted my thoughts.

'So, Dr Daniels, what medication had you been prescribing him? Did you start him on any new medication just before he died?'

Bloody hell, I hadn't even thought about that. Could some wayward prescribing on my part have contributed to his death? Suddenly, I sharply switched back into self-preservation mode. The medications I had prescribed to Mr Dawkins were all fairly common, but as the coroner was hinting, they could have all potentially killed him: the aspirin could have caused a bleed from his stomach; the diabetes medication could have dropped his blood sugar causing him to die of hypoglycaemia; the blood pressure tablets might have caused him to faint and bash his head; and the combination of his cholesterol tablets and excessive drinking might have given him liver failure.

I carefully explained all the medications to the coroner, and as

I put the phone down I sat quietly stewing in a light sweat, again wondering about my potential influence over another man's life. I took another good look through Mr Dawkins' notes. Much as I was annoyed by the computer record's constant flashing up of targets, one number did jump out at me from Mr Dawkins' records. His risk score of dying in the next 10 years was 47 per cent. Clearly a stupid statistic to remain on the records of a man already dead, but basically the computer was working out the risk of him having a heart attack or stroke based on his weight, blood pressure, smoking history, diabetes, cholesterol and age. The statistic was basically stating that despite being young, his other risk factors made dying not that unlikely. I was still a bit worried that the medications I had prescribed might have killed him, but I was now also considering that perhaps his death had resulted in me not having treated his risk factors aggressively enough.

I took a good look through his notes and was reassured by the amount of time the doctors and nurses at this surgery had spent advising him to stop smoking and lose weight and take better control of his diabetes. We were constantly trying to get his blood pressure under control and, to be honest, I'm not really sure what more we could have done for him.

I still had a nervous wait for the result of the post-mortem. When it came, it was no surprise to learn that he had died from a massive heart attack, but I can't pretend that my initial reaction wasn't relief that I had played no untoward part in his demise. In some ways we should consider it a success that we now see the death of a man in his 50s as such a shocking event. It didn't used to be, and it is because doctors and patients have got better at reducing the risk factors. I phoned up his poor widow to offer my condolences and support and she asked me if she could book into our stop-smoking clinic.

Mr Goodson

'HELLO MR GOODSON. CAN YOU HEAR ME? IT'S THE DOCTOR.'

I was kneeling on a doorstep in the pouring rain shouting through a letter box.

I had received a phone call that morning from Mr Goodson's worried niece. She had been receiving increasingly odd letters from him over the past few months and wanted me to go and make sure he was okay. At this point, I wondered whether as his closest relative she might want to demonstrate her concern by visiting herself, but she gently pointed out that she was phoning me from her home in New Zealand, so as his GP responsibility for his wellbeing fell to me.

Mr Goodson doesn't have a phone and he had previously always communicated by writing kindly letters to his niece in New Zealand. Recently the letters had been becoming increasingly paranoid in nature, warning her of a conspiracy regarding a dangerous network of computers controlled by the British royal family and the Kennedy family in America. According to him they were plotting to control the world by placing a grid of electromagnetic energy around it that would have power over our minds.

In the most recent letter she had received, Mr Goodson had accused her of being part of the conspiracy too, and it was at this point that she decided to give me a ring.

I hadn't met Mr Goodson before. He had been registered at our surgery for years but, despite being 73 years old, his computer records suggested that he didn't have any health complaints. He didn't answer our letters advising him to come in for flu jabs and health checks and so up until now we had always respected his choice to keep away and left him in peace. The phone call this morning changed all that and I couldn't ignore his niece's concerns. It would appear that his paranoid thoughts were likely to have been ongoing for some months now, so there wasn't any real reason to rush round that same day, but just last month I'd discovered that one of my patients had lain dead on his sofa for four months without anyone realising. I didn't want another of my patients to suffer the same fate, hence the situation I now found myself in, shouting through a letter box in the pouring rain.

After five minutes of yelling and banging on the door, I was on the verge of giving up and hoping he was simply out rather than lying dead somewhere inside. I knocked on his next-door neighbour's door, who helpfully told me that she was fairly sure he hadn't been out in days, so I returned for a few last desperate shouts through the letter box.

'IF YOU DON'T LET ME IN I'M GOING TO HAVE TO BREAK THE DOOR DOWN.'

This last-ditch attempt to persuade Mr Goodson to open the door was an empty threat. I really didn't have the strength or inclination to break down a front door, but just as I was ready to give up and go back to the surgery, I thought I heard some stirring from within the house. I kneeled down again on the doorstep to peer through the letter box and to my surprise this time I saw a pair of eyes staring straight back at me.

'You can't come in,' he told me calmly. 'You're contaminated.'

'Er, I don't think I am,' I answered feebly, suddenly a bit thrown that I was having this bizarre conversation through a letter box.

'Yes you are,' Mr Goodson responded confidently. 'What do you want anyway?'

'I'm Dr Daniels, your GP. Your niece called me. She's worried about you.'

'She's contaminated too. I tried to warn her but she wouldn't listen.'

'Can I just come in for a chat?'

'You'll need to decontaminate first. Hold on.'

With that, Mr Goodson stood up and shuffled away from the door. Some moments later a nearly empty and very old bottle of Johnson's baby oil was pushed out through the letter box and landed at my feet.

'The electromagnetic rays can't get through this. It repels them,' he explained.

Looking at the grubby bottle, I wondered how far I should go along with Mr Goodson's delusions. I tried rationally suggesting that I had already washed my hands carefully before leaving the surgery, but Mr Goodson made it very clear that this wouldn't be sufficient. There was a limit to the amount of time that I was prepared to spend shouting through a door while getting drenched by a November downpour, so I gave in and picked up the bottle of baby oil. I made a show of rubbing some of the lotion over my hands while Mr Goodson watched me suspiciously through the letter box.

'Right, I'm all, erm … decontaminated now.'

'Your face isn't. That needs doing too.'

I looked down at the grubby-looking bottle and wondered at its age. Did I really want to rub this stuff on to my face? Johnson's baby oil is harmless enough, but I couldn't be entirely sure that, in his paranoia, Mr Goodson hadn't added less savoury ingredients to the bottle. I stood for a few moments, trying to come up with a better method of gaining entry than smearing this stuff on my face, but when nothing came to mind I reluctantly rubbed the cream over my face, and to my relief I heard the clunk of his front door unlocking.

Once inside I was amazed that Mr Goodson really thought that some sort of contamination was going to arise from the outside world rather than from the filthy state of the interior. It took a while for my eyes to adjust to the darkness, but once they had I was greeted by a stark and miserable sight. Mr Goodson himself was in a terrible state. He had clearly once been a tall man but now he was hunched over and his ragged looking shirt and trousers were baggy on his bony frame. The floor was a bare lino, sticky with grime, and the walls were brown from the tar staining of decades of cigarette smoke. Plates of half-eaten meals and empty food packaging were piled high in one corner of the living room and an awful stench of what smelled like sour milk seeped into the pit of my stomach making me want to gag. All his windows were blocked out by rows of tin foil and empty egg boxes, which were crudely Sellotaped to the glass in what I could only imagine was another attempt by Mr Goodson to deflect the electromagnetic forces he so feared.

'Do you have a computer, Doctor?'

'Well, yes.'

'You need to get rid of it right away. They're sending messages through it.'

'What, like emails?'

Mr Goodson looked at me blankly and I could see that the concept of an email was completely alien to him; we stood in silence for a few moments, with Mr Goodson shuffling around me, his suspicious gaze fixed on my face. Having made such an effort to gain entry to his house, now that I was in, I felt at a bit of a loss as to what to do next. I had successfully confirmed that Mr Goodson was alive and also that he was floridly paranoid and delusional. He was clearly very suspicious of me, so my next step was going to be tricky. I decided I needed to try to gain his trust, but cordial small talk has never really been something I'm any good at.

'So, how have you been?' I asked with false brightness.

'I'm just trying to stay alive, Doctor.'

'Yes, erm, aren't we all …? Pretty bloody awful weather, isn't it?'

'Water helps conduct the radiation. It can spread in rain water.'

The small talk wasn't really getting me very far, so I decided to try to address the elephant in the room.

'So, why do you think everyone is contaminated?'

Mr Goodson went on to describe in some detail his fears about global plots and bizarre conspiracies. Such was the intensity of his paranoia that I knew that there would be no benefit in trying to challenge his beliefs. Mr Goodson needed to have antipsychotic medication and ideally be admitted to a psychiatric unit where he could be safe and looked after until his delusional paranoia settled. I gently introduced the subject of him taking some medication to help make the unpleasant thoughts go away, but he wasn't having any of it. As far as he was concerned, he was the only one who accurately understood the truth and it was the rest of us who were unwell.

Sectioning is not a decision that anyone takes lightly and it really is used as a last resort, when there are no other feasible options available. Some people manage to stay living independently at home with quite marked chronic delusional symptoms, but Mr Goodson's symptoms were such that it was preventing him from being able to look after himself. Once someone's illness leads to the potential to harm themselves or others, the person can be judged as unwell enough to be admitted to a psychiatric unit against their will. Sensibly, such a grave decision isn't one that I'm allowed to make alone. It requires the joint decision of a GP, a psychiatrist and a specialist social worker, and so when I returned to the surgery I made some arrangements to return the next day with the cavalry.

The following day I met the psychiatrist and social worker outside Mr Goodson's house. They looked a little surprised when I took from my bag a bottle of Johnson's baby oil that I had taken from my own bathroom cabinet that morning. When we knocked on Mr Goodson's door, he made me push my bottle of baby lotion through the letter box. After it passed his careful inspection, it was posted back out and he intently watched all three of us smear ourselves with the stuff before letting us in.

My biggest fear at that point was that Mr Goodson would point-blank refuse to be admitted to hospital, leaving us no choice but to get the police involved to forcibly detain him. In his paranoid state, this would be terrifying for him, and he was in such a physically frail state that if he put up a fight I was scared he might get badly injured.

Fortunately, the social worker was brilliant. She had a very calming way about her, and without either colluding with his delusions or openly refuting them, she managed to persuade Mr Goodson that he would be safer and better off under the care of the mental health team. It took some time to reassure him about levels of contamination in her car, but eventually off they went and he was able to get the care and treatment that he needed.

Psychosis is a terrifying condition for the sufferer. The strange thoughts and paranoid ideas that can seem ridiculous to us feel absolutely real to the poor person with the condition. The antipsychotic medications available aren't perfect, but they do help clear away the delusions and return people to reality. Since starting these drugs, Mr Goodson is much better. He is still undeniably eccentric, but the tin foil has been taken down from the windows and I no longer have to smother myself in baby oil in order to gain entrance to his house. Most importantly, he feels safe again and is able to live something resembling a normal life.

Mr Raymond

As a patient Mr Raymond asked little of me. He rarely came into the surgery and when he did he was courteous and undemanding. He had spent some time in prison for child sex offences and each time I met him, I had to try to force myself to be professional and not let the fact that he was a paedophile cloud the way I treated him. My job as his doctor was to treat him with impartiality and compassion as my patient, rather than judge him as a person. This sounds straightforward enough, but I will admit that I found it difficult. He had recently been diagnosed with diabetes and was a model patient, attending all his appointments and sticking to his new diet and medication regime.

'So what can I do for you today, Mr Raymond?'

'Well, the nurse mostly looks after my diabetes, Doctor, but I was too embarrassed to mention this little problem I've been having to her.'

'What's that then?'

'I think the diabetes is affecting my erections. I can't seem to get them any more and I was wondering if I could try some Viagra?'

The diabetes may well have been affecting his erections. There were other possible causes too, but Mr Raymond was aware that now he had been diagnosed with diabetes he was entitled to free Viagra on the NHS. I asked a few more questions and even examined him, but overall his complaint was fairly standard. With most of our diabetic male patients, I wouldn't have thought twice about prescribing some Viagra or something similar, but for obvious reasons, I had reservations with Mr Raymond.

I knew that Raymond had sexually abused young children in the past. He had served his time and I had no reason to believe he was re-offending or even considering it. Perhaps he was completely rehabilitated and was in a healthy loving relationship with a consenting adult. The problem was I couldn't help but worry that my prescribing him Viagra could potentially lead to further abuse of children. I wasn't sure if Mr Raymond knew that I had a record of his previous offences, although my apparent awkwardness may well have made it fairly obvious.

'Do you have a regular partner?' I asked, attempting to enquire as if making light conversation.

'Er, no, not exactly. I just, you know, like to still be able to have erections by myself, if you catch my drift.'

After a few moments of an uncomfortable silence, I broke it with some honesty.

'Look, Mr Raymond, I know that you have a criminal record for sex offences in the past and I need to just make sure where I stand legally before I consider prescribing you Viagra.'

'That's all behind me, Doctor. I did a whole programme when I was inside. With this bad back of mine I barely even leave my flat, let alone get myself into any trouble.'

'Look, I'll find out the rules about this sort of thing and then I can decide. Come back and see me next week.'

I was relieved when Mr Raymond left, but I still couldn't work out what to do. Mr Raymond had once abused children. The legal system had deemed him safe for release from prison and were it not for his medical condition he might well be able to have completely normal erections. I had no evidence to suggest that by me prescribing Viagra, children would be put at risk. What if he wasn't abusing children, but was looking at child pornography? Would that make a difference? Perhaps he still fantasised about children but just used his own imagination to get aroused? When do I start having to be concerned about the ethics of this as his doctor? At what stage should I be allowed to pass judgment on when a man should or shouldn't be permitted to have erections?

I decided to do some research on the matter, which is a posh way of saying that I Googled 'prescribing Viagra to paedophiles'. The first pages that cropped up were about a French man who raped a young boy after being prescribed Viagra by his doctor in 2007. This served to prove that my greatest fear could potentially become a reality and it successfully increased my paranoia. Doctors belong to a defence union which can give advice at times like this. I called them up and the medico-legal expert told me that unless I had reasonable cause to fear that Mr Raymond was an active risk to children, I couldn't justify refusing the prescription. She also told me that if I did refuse to prescribe him Viagra, Mr Raymond would be within his rights to make a complaint and take legal action against me. I documented this very carefully and was relieved that the law was so clear. I'm sure that many would be disgusted at the idea of a convicted paedophile receiving Viagra on the NHS, but the decision was out of my hands. To my relief, Mr Raymond never turned up for his follow-up appointment. Perhaps he was too embarrassed, or possibly, most likely, he bought some cheap Viagra online instead.

Hannah

The overwhelming desire to become a mother was so strong in Hannah it was almost palpable. It seemed to ooze from every pore of her skin. Ever since she had been my patient it was pretty much the only thing that she ever came in to talk to me about. All other physical ailments were put aside in order to concentrate on that most basic of human desires: to have a baby.

Hannah was now 42, and as each month passed her dream of motherhood slipped further and further from her grasp. There is plenty of talk in the media about career women putting their jobs first only to find that they have left it too late to have a baby. This wasn't the case with Hannah. She would have happily started a family in her 20s, but she had quite simply never met the right guy. When she reached 37, Hannah decided against risking her chance of motherhood by waiting for Mr Right, and chose instead to embark on fertility treatments as a single woman. Our initial consultations were about the pros and cons of using an anonymous donor versus using the sperm of a generous gay friend. At first she battled to get funding for IVF on the NHS but failed, and so instead used all her savings to have cycles of fertility treatment privately. With each cycle came the drugs and the injections, followed by the hope and then, finally, in Hannah's case, the overwhelming disappointment.

My job throughout all of this was simply to support her. I helped out practically by occasionally organising blood tests and letters to explain time off work, but mostly I was another shoulder to cry on when all the hope turned to despair. Hannah was putting her entire life on hold in order to have a baby. She stopped going out or having holidays. She spent every penny on fertility treatment. She turned down a promotion at work, because she didn't want the stress of more responsibility affecting her chance to conceive. She even turned down a few nice blokes who asked her out, knowing that trying to get pregnant via donor sperm while in the early stages of a new relationship was just too weird.

Hannah was aware of how much the IVF was taking over her life. She had told me that she just wanted to know she had tried everything she could to get pregnant and if it hadn't happened by the time she hit 40, she would take a deep breath and move on with her life.

However, when her 40th birthday came and went, she couldn't quite let go. 'I'm still having periods, Dr Daniels, and I feel healthy!' she explained to me. 'I couldn't live with myself if I hadn't tried everything I could to conceive.'

At the age of 41, after eight unsuccessful cycles, she had spent a total of £40,000. Her credit cards were maxed out and her flat had been remortgaged twice. She had borrowed money from her sister and mum. Finally, she came in to tell me that she had given up.

'It's a relief really, Doctor. It took so much out of me physically and emotionally. Even if I had the money I'm not sure I could put myself through another cycle. I've decided to adopt. There are children who need mothers and it seems selfish and stupid to be desperately trying to make a new baby when there are plenty of babies in the world who need a mother.'

The adoption process isn't easy either, but at least it was a positive move rather than the continual pain of IVF. We went through the forms together and I completed the questions relating to her health. Up until the IVF, Hannah had been completely healthy, but during the last round of treatment they had found a cyst on her ovary that needed further investigation. Before I could complete the adoption paperwork, she needed to have her cyst investigated. I referred her to a gynaecology consultant and the news came back that it was ovarian cancer.

At first glance it might seem as though the IVF had saved her, as it was a scan during the IVF procedure that had picked up the mass on the ovary before she had any symptoms. In reality, it was highly likely that her fertility treatment had caused the cancer. The medication prescribed to stimulate the ovaries at least doubles the risk of ovarian cancer. So, after finally thinking that she was over all the unpleasant medical procedures that had plagued her during her fertility treatments, Hannah would now have to go through a whole lot more, this time to try to save her own life rather than create a new one.

A year later, battered and exhausted, Hannah came back to see me, having finally been given the all-clear by the cancer doctors; the ovarian tumour had gone. She now wanted to get back on track with the adoption agency.

It was at this point that I had to break the awful news to her that now that she was a 'cancer survivor', they were unlikely to place a child with her for adoption. The risk of the cancer returning was still quite high and as a single mother if this did happen a child placed with her could become an orphan. I really didn't think she'd be allowed to adopt a child now and I thought it best to be honest with her straight away.

Finally, Hannah's grief erupted. The thought of adopting had been getting her through the horrors of her cancer treatment and now this door was closing on her too. She was absolutely devastated.

It was several months before I saw Hannah again. She literally bounced through my door like a Labrador puppy.

'I'm pregnant,' she beamed.

'What?'

'You heard me. I'm pregnant!'

'How?'

'Well, I'm not sure if you remember but my dad died a year ago and we finally got his affairs in order. I inherited some money and my sister agreed to go with me to a fertility clinic out in India. She donated an egg and well ... *voilà*. I didn't want to tell you that we were going, because I thought you might try to put me off.'

'Well, I might have tried, but well, wow! Congratulations! How many weeks are you?'

'I've just had my 12-week scan and everything looks fine. I didn't really need to see you about anything in particular but I just wanted to come and let you know.'

'I'm so pleased for you, Hannah, and I can't wait to meet your new baby in the flesh in six months' time!'

I could barely take the smile off my face for the rest of that day.

Ted

If anyone asks me the worst thing about being a doctor, my answer is always immediate: for me, it's the constant fear of making a mistake. Every July a letter from the General Medical Council falls on my doormat. It is always a request to renew my annual subscription, but without fail, when I see who the letter is from, my heart races as I wonder if this could be the summons calling me to explain my incompetent actions to a courtroom full of grieving relatives and snarling journalists. It's a fear that never goes away. It is something that every doctor has to learn to live with.

I was once three days into a holiday in Mexico when I woke up in a cold sweat, terrified that I had forgotten to do something for a particular patient sitting in a hospital ward 5,000 miles away. I couldn't go back to sleep until I had called the ward to make sure the patient was okay. I was genuinely worried about that patient, but I can't deny that there was a large helping of self-preservation in my fear. Making a mistake could cost me my job. Still, despite the general consensus that doctors are only in it for the money, we do care about our patients, and the idea that someone could come to harm because of my error is horrifying.

A surgeon knows that if he accidentally snips an artery when trying to remove a kidney the patient could die within seconds on the table in front of him. As a GP my mistakes are less acutely dramatic, but the potential consequences of my actions could be just as grave. Any headache could be a brain tumour, any feverish child could have meningitis and, as I discovered last year, any cough could be lung cancer.

Last April Ted came to see me with a bad knee. We had a chat about painkillers and I referred him to a physiotherapist. As he was leaving he asked me if there was anything I could do about his smoker's cough. I suggested he gave up smoking, and he shrugged and walked out the door. Eight months later he was admitted to the emergency department with a collapsed lung due to lung cancer. When I looked back at the medical notes I made at that last appointment with me, I hung my head in shame. I wrote plenty about his knee pain and then at the very end it read: '*Cough. Smoker. Advised to stop smoking.*' That was it: I hadn't listened to his lungs, I hadn't asked about weight loss or coughing up blood, and I didn't request the chest X-ray that might have diagnosed his cancer earlier and saved his life. I even looked through the notes of some of the other patients I saw that afternoon. I spent nearly 30 minutes talking to a 20-year-old law student about her numerous self-diagnosed food intolerances, yet when Ted told me about his cough, I short-changed him with just a few seconds of my time.

I was dreading seeing Ted again when he came into see me after his diagnosis. However, when I apologised for not picking up his illness earlier, he laughed. 'Dr Daniels, it was me who smoked all them cigarettes for all those years. I can't blame you for me getting this disease. I was dreading coming in to see you as I thought you'd be cross with me for not taking your advice to give up the fags sooner. I was expecting you to say "I told you so", not "I'm sorry"!'

I tried to explain my culpability: 'But if I had sent you for a chest X-ray sooner, the cancer might have been curable.'

Ted gave me a generous smile. 'Don't blame yourself, Doctor. I don't.' With that, he left. Despite his generous forgiveness, every time I saw Ted I was awash with guilt.

There is a bad joke about doctors being able to *bury* their mistakes. This wasn't the case with Ted. I saw him at work, but I also bumped into him in the supermarket with his wife. I even spotted him at the football with his grandson. It was as if he was everywhere I looked, and each time we met, his obvious deterioration was a reminder of my error. Even now that he has died, Ted's wife comes to see me regularly. She remains oddly trusting of my medical opinion and completely unaware of the massive guilt that bubbles to the surface of my consciousness with her every visit.

The fear of making a mistake is indeed a terrible part of being a doctor, but on reflection actually *making* a mistake is truly the worst part of the job.

Should we name and shame doctors who make mistakes?

I'm not the only GP to have made a mistake; compensation payouts for medical negligence are going up, not just the number of cases but in the cost of the payouts. As a way of combating this, it has been suggested by the government that doctors should be named and shamed by publishing our mistakes and performance data online. The idea is that this will allow patients to choose their GP based on his or her track record, and that the resulting possibility of losing 'customers' (patients) will motivate us to improve.

It might also be suggested that the best way for GPs to reduce the chances of missing a serious diagnosis is for GPs to have a very low threshold for referring patients on for specialist care. The problem with this is that we are also under massive pressure to keep our referral figures down. The NHS is able to keep costs down in part because GPs successfully triage the 'worried well' away from busy hospitals and costly specialists. High levels of referrals are expensive and push up waiting time. Often those referred are already better by the time they see the specialist or could be equally well treated by their GP. There may well come a time when those doctors who are over-eager to send their patients to hospital will be penalised for using up too many resources.

GPs are under pressure from all sides, but at the same time there are some slip-ups for which we have to step up and take responsibility. I made a mistake with Ted and it is one for which I will hold up my hands up. If the current proposals go ahead, would my patients have the right to know about that previous blunder? Would they register with another doctor as a result? In an attempt at redemption I now ask all my smoking patients if they have a cough. If they have even the slightest throat tickle, they get sent for a chest X-ray. My practice has changed because I am scared that a future patient might come to harm due to my misjudgment. I'm not convinced that the added forfeit of damaging performance stats would really make that much difference.

I am ready to own up and take responsibility for my mistakes, but wouldn't we all agree that the real key is trying to prevent errors being made in the future? Rather than spending money on dredging up my past in order to rank me in a series of performance data statistics, perhaps it would be better to look for more positive ways to prevent future slip-ups. In our practice we have found talking openly about our errors helps. If a patient had a serious condition that was missed, all the staff look through the notes together to try to work out what we could do differently next time. If there is a field of medicine we feel our knowledge levels are lacking in, we encourage each other to get up to date on the latest research.

There were 300 million GP consultations in England in 2011 and just over 7,000 complaints made to the General Medical Council. That works out at around one serious complaint for every 42,000 consultations. Most GPs are good at their job and this is reflected in the ongoing high levels of trust in our profession. When mistakes are made we need to take responsibility for them, but we should also be encouraged to learn from them in an open and supportive environment. It really doesn't seem to me that name and shame proposals are offering this. I would also suggest that they don't really tackle the issue of persistently poor GPs either. If a doctor can't learn from their errors and makes the same mistake time after time then surely something more serious needs to be done than simply publicly denouncing them on a government website?

Pseudocyesis

'I think I'm losing my baby,' wailed the lady sitting in front of me.

Karen was not one of my regular patients and had only registered with our surgery that week. She explained to me that she was 25 weeks pregnant and that up until now her pregnancy had been completely normal.

'Every day for the last six weeks I've felt my baby move, but I've felt nothing since last night,' she anxiously told me.

'I'm sure he's fine in there, he's probably just having a lie-in,' I chirped optimistically. 'We'll have a little listen.'

I was fairly convinced Karen was just having first-time pregnancy jitters and I was looking forward to reassuring her with that lovely sound of a baby's heartbeat. With Karen up on the couch, I squeezed some gel onto her tummy and moved my Doppler probe around listening for the baby's heartbeat.

We both remained silent as we listened for the trace of life. Every so often, between the white noise of interference I could make out a pulse, but it was the slow whooshing sound of Karen's own arteries pulsating rather than the much faster clicking sound of a baby's heartbeat. We endured an awful 10 minutes of searching, but however much I tweaked and moved the probe, I couldn't hear the reassuring beat that would let us know her baby was alive. I finally gave up and Karen got off the couch.

'Look, Karen, it might just be my Doppler machine or perhaps your baby's lying at a funny angle or something. I'm going to call the obstetric doctor at the hospital and ask them to see you this afternoon. They'll do a proper scan and find out what's going on.'

Just as I picked up my phone to call the hospital, I heard a wail from Karen.

'Oh my god, Doctor, I think I'm going into labour!'

Karen started screaming in pain and I dialled 999.

The paramedics were with us within minutes.

As she panted and groaned, I helped Karen into the ambulance, tears of fear and pain running down her face. As soon as she was safely on her way to hospital, I called the obstetric registrar to warn him of Karen's imminent arrival.

I carried on with my surgery that afternoon, but all the while I was thinking about Karen and wondering what was happening to her. Going into labour at 25 weeks is much too early and although I've heard of the odd baby surviving when born that premature, the odds really aren't great. The fact that I couldn't hear the baby's heartbeat on my probe made me feel even more despairing of the poor little mite's chances. Miscarriages before 12 weeks are common and heartbreaking, but losing a pregnancy after 25 long weeks must be absolutely horrendous.

As I was sorting out the last of my paperwork at the end of surgery, I decided to call the obstetric registrar at the hospital to find out what was happening.

'Are you the GP that sent that woman in with the premature labour?'

'Yes, that was me. How is she?'

'Well, you didn't quite get the diagnosis right.'

'What do you mean?'

'She had pseudocyesis.'

'Oh … could you just remind me what that is?'

The obstetric registrar paused for effect and then gave a sigh. 'It was a pretend pregnancy. As her GP we thought you might have managed to at least do a pregnancy test before getting all excited and sending the nee-naws screaming round with the flashing blue lights.' With that the obstetric doctor put the phone down, no doubt greatly amused by his successful belittling of me.

Normally I would be irritated at such an unpleasant dressing down by some smug little upstart, but I was absolutely dumbstruck that Karen hadn't been pregnant. Why had she lied to me? Why had she put herself through such a bizarre and ultimately humiliating experience? My patients fib to me all the time. Mostly they lie about how much they drink or try to con me into believing that their valium prescription had been stolen and they needed some more. It's been a long time since I routinely took all my patients' declarations to be wholly truthful, but when Karen told me she was 25 weeks pregnant, I took it completely at face value.

Shocked and upset, I turned to the internet for support and was amazed by how common and powerful false pregnancies can be. For some women the overwhelming desire to believe they are pregnant can even cause their brain to produce the release of hormones that can lead to real pregnancy symptoms such as nausea and bloating. The hormones can stop periods like a real pregnancy would, often fooling everyone around them. Admittedly, the obstetric registrar was right, a pregnancy test would have given the game away, but I have a sneaky suspicion that they only realised that Karen wasn't really pregnant once they got out the ultrasound scanner.

As a doctor it is never nice to know that you've got something completely wrong, but there is an odd reassurance in knowing you are not the only one to have made that mistake. Apparently an obstetrician in the US had been fooled into taking things one step further when a woman with a false pregnancy came in to see her claiming to be nine months pregnant. When the doctor couldn't find the baby's heartbeat, the woman was rushed straight to surgery and given an emergency caesarean section in a desperate attempt to save the imaginary baby. It was only when they cut her open and dug around in her abdomen for a bit that they discovered there was in fact no baby to save. Makes my mistake seem relatively trivial in comparison.

I would love to have spoken to Karen again. I wasn't angry, just confused. Did she really think that she was pregnant? Was it part of some sort of odd delusional belief that was part of a wider mental health problem? Was it just some peculiar form of attention-seeking behaviour? Sadly, I've never found out, because Karen never came back to see me.

Playing God

I'd been called out for a home visit to see Miss Blumenthal, a 94-year-old lady who was living in one of our local nursing homes. I had never met her before, but I had visited other patients at this home and it didn't have the best of reputations. The nurses who worked there were nice enough, but the organisation was poor and the big company who owned the home seemed to run it purely to make the maximum profit. It was always understaffed and the nurses and carers were paid a pittance. Any competent members of staff moved on quickly to better employers, leaving a few stragglers who would perhaps struggle to find any work elsewhere.

I stood ringing the doorbell for several minutes before Carmela, the nurse in charge, finally opened the front door for me. She looked very flustered.

'Sorry, Doctor, lunchtime always very busy, busy.'

Carmela was Filipino and her English really wasn't great.

'So, what's been going on then, with Miss Blumenthal?'

'Miss Blumenthal not been eating or drinking for last few days,' she told me, reading from a scrap of paper she'd pulled out of the pocket of her tunic.

'Anything else you can tell me?'

Carmela studied her scrap of paper for any further information but there was clearly none. 'I've been off the last few days,' she shrugged.

'Best go and see her then, shall we?'

Carmela led me through a network of corridors and fire doors before we reached Miss Blumenthal's room.

'Hello Miss Blumenthal, I'm the doctor.'

Miss Blumenthal opened her eyes briefly and mumbled something in a foreign language.

'She used to sometimes speak to us in English, but she doesn't any more. She only speaks to us in Polish now.'

This wasn't unusual in people with Alzheimer's. Even if they are completely fluent in a second language, as they slip further into dementia, they almost always lapse into speaking only their mother tongue. Carmela was wrong about the language she was mumbling in, though.

'She's not speaking Polish, that's Yiddish.'

Carmela looked at me oddly: 'But is say on her record that she is Polish.'

'She may well have been born in Poland, but she's Jewish and the language she is speaking is Yiddish. It's actually closer to German than Polish.'

Carmela nodded, but looked at me suspiciously, as if I was trying to play some sort of odd trick on her. I sat on Miss Blumenthal's bed and held her hand. She opened her eyes and I smiled at her but her look remained completely vacant. She mumbled something, again in Yiddish. Yiddish was the first language of my great-grandparents. It was once the common language of Jews all over Eastern Europe, but has now pretty much completely died out. The only words of Yiddish I know are 'shmuck' and 'chutzpah', neither of which were likely to have any great value in the current situation.

I turned my attention back to Carmela. 'So, Miss Blumenthal doesn't communicate much these days, but what can she do when she is well?'

Carmela again looked at me as if I was asking some sort of trick question.

'I've never met Miss Blumenthal before, so I need to know how she is normally,' I explained patiently. 'For example, a couple of weeks ago what could she do?'

I was met with further awkward silence, so I tried to clarify things further.

'Could she walk and eat and go to the toilet by herself?'

'Oh no, Doctor,' Carmela replied, relieved that she had finally got to grips with my line of questioning. 'She used to sit in lounge, but not any more.'

'So she's bed bound.'

'Yes, Doctor.'

'And she's incontinent of urine and faeces.'

'Yes, Doctor.'

'And occasionally she mumbles away in her language but doesn't seem to understand you?'

'Yes, Doctor.'

'And you have to spoon-feed her puréed meals?'

'Yes, Doctor, but last few days she is refusing to eat or drink.'

Carmela was smiling now, relieved that we seemed to have at least partly bridged what had once appeared to be an impassable chasm in our ability to communicate.

'Does she have any family?'

'Nobody. There is a nephew in Canada but we haven't heard from him in years.'

Miss Blumenthal closed her eyes again and lay passively as I examined her.

As I rolled up her sleeve to check her blood pressure, I saw a series of green numbers tattooed on the inside of her left forearm. I stopped cold. It was a concentration camp tattoo. I had only seen one once before, but it was unmistakable. She opened her eyes and caught me staring dumbstruck at her forearm, but there was still not the slightest glimmer of expression in her face. In the relative peace of her nursing home, I couldn't possibly imagine what horrors she must have witnessed 70 or so years ago in a Nazi concentration camp.

I remember as a medical student speaking to another patient who survived a concentration camp. He described a Nazi doctor separating the new arrivals into those who looked well enough to work and those who looked too weak. He was only 15 years old at the time, but the doctor chose him to live and placed his parents and little sister in the line that went straight to the gas chambers. I spent many hours after that conversation wondering how any doctor goes from learning about saving lives to choosing which people live and which die in a death camp. Looking at Miss Blumenthal's tattoo, I wondered if she had faced some such doctor all those years ago. Had that doctor looked her up and down and chosen her to live?

It was now my turn to make a decision about Miss Blumenthal's future. It was a different time and place, but in some ways there were stark similarities in the decision-making process. I was a doctor deciding whether I believed Miss Blumenthal might be able to survive the next few months. I was having to try to place some sort of value on her life and then make a decision based on my conclusion. Unlike the Nazi doctor, I'd like to think that my decision was going to be based on compassion and kindness, but it was still a massive decision to make, the significance of which wasn't lost on me.

'Does she need to go to hospital, Doctor?' Carmela asked me.

'Well, yes and no. She has stopped taking anything orally, so unless she goes to hospital for intravenous fluids, she'll get dehydrated and die.'

'I'll call an ambulance, Doctor.'

'Hold on. She's 94 years old with advanced dementia and very little of what could be considered quality of life. She can't walk or communicate or toilet herself. She may also die in hospital regardless of the fluids. It might be kindest to keep her here rather than have her end up on a trolley in a busy emergency department.'

'What do you want to do, Doctor?'

'Well, really we should make a team decision. You and the staff here have been looking after Miss Blumenthal for some years now and knew her when she was less unwell and less demented. Have you any thoughts about what she might have wanted in this sort of situation? Did she make any sort of living will?'

Carmela continued to look at me with an expression of confusion. The idea that she could and should be part of this important decision-making process had clearly never occurred to her. As far as she was concerned, I was the doctor and this was my judgment to call and mine alone.

I had been working in A&E only the day before and it was absolute mayhem. There were trolleys of patients stacked up in the corridor and security guards wrestling with burly drunks in the waiting room. If one of my patients really needs hospital treatment, then the busyness of the hospital wouldn't be a deciding factor, but I really wasn't convinced that hospital was the best place for Miss Blumenthal – she faced what was undoubtedly the final phase of her life. Whatever my misgivings about the nursing home, her room was calm and peaceful, the surroundings were familiar and the staff were caring.

'Okay, I'm not going to send her to hospital. I'm going to sign a "not for resuscitation" form and the plan is to keep her comfortable here.'

'What if she gets worse, Doctor?'

'She probably will get worse. I want you to make sure she's comfy, encourage her to take fluids and food if she's not refusing, and if she seems to be getting into any sort of distress or pain, I'll write up a syringe driver for morphine.'

Doctors are often accused of playing God. My decision not to send Miss Blumenthal to hospital could be perceived as giving her a death sentence, but I don't see it that way. I was simply accepting that she was coming to the natural end of her life. In an ideal world the patient, family and medical staff are collectively involved in these sorts of tough end-of-life decisions. Unfortunately, sometimes that just isn't possible and someone like me has to step up and make a judgment.

End-of-life decisions are never easy, but I couldn't help feeling that my decision was even more emotive given the struggle for survival Miss Blumenthal had faced all those years previously. I knew nothing of her life between then and now but I'd like to think it had been worth the fight. Perhaps reaching 94 years old should even be considered a poignant victory over the evil that had nearly ended her life 70 years earlier.

Simon

'Yeah, just a quick one for you, Doctor. I need you to refer me to see a psychiatrist.'

'Right, so why's that then?'

'Is that any of your business? I just need to get referred and then you can get on with your day and I can get on with mine.'

'It doesn't really work like that. If I'm going to send you to see a psychiatrist I need to be able to explain in the referral letter what specialist help you need. I need to have done an assessment of your mental health and to consider that the severity of your condition is beyond what I as a GP can manage.'

Simon, the young man in front of me, was well dressed and held my gaze with a calm self-assuredness that bordered on cockiness. He didn't look depressed, anxious or psychotic. He had never been to see me before with any mental health problems and I couldn't for the life of me fathom his sudden desire to see a psychiatrist.

'Look, Doctor, I'll be straight with you. I've got myself into a spot of bother and my solicitor says that the judge will look on it favourably if I can show that I'm addressing my anger issues.'

'What have you been charged with?'

'Well, they're trying to pin me with racially aggravated GBH, but it was self-defence and I'm no racist. I mean, I went out with a half-Chinese girl once, so how can I be racist?'

As Simon aggressively declared his innocence, I discreetly tapped his name into Google and read the local newspaper's record of events. According to witnesses, he had had a dispute with a taxi driver, who he had pulled out of the car and punched unconscious. Several witnesses stated that as his victim was lying face down in the road Simon continued to kick him in the head while calling him a fucking dirty Paki. Clearly everyone is innocent until proven guilty, but I was struggling to find empathy with the man sitting in front of me. He was still blaming everyone else rather than showing any remorse and he certainly wasn't expressing a genuine desire to address any underlying mental health issues he might have.

'Look, Doctor, I could lose everything here. If I get done for this I'll lose my job and I'll have a criminal record for life. I could go down for two to three years.'

I managed to resist the overwhelming desire to tell him that he should have thought of that before he decided to kick a man's head in. I could feel my blood pressure rising and a little voice at the back of my head told me that I was letting my emotions get in the way of the consultation. I needed to treat this man with impartiality and without judgment. A legal declaration of his guilt or innocence was yet to be made and as his doctor it was my duty to treat his medical needs regardless of anything else. I took a deep breath, and blocking out any personal feelings of dislike I had towards him, I returned to thinking about the primary medical needs of my patient. He wasn't unwell physically and although it could be argued that anyone with such violent tendencies must have some underlying mental health issues, these clearly weren't currently something that he had any desire to address. In summary, I could justifiably tell him to bugger off.

'I'm not going to be able to refer you to see a psychiatrist on the NHS. The psychiatrists have got a really busy caseload as it is with lots of very mentally unwell people in this town. I would only refer you to see a psychiatrist if your mental health merited it, not because it might help you in a court case.'

'Look, the court case is tomorrow. Once I get off the charge I won't even go to the appointment. I just need to have a letter from you stating that I've been referred.'

'I'm sorry, but it's not going to happen.'

For the first time I saw Simon losing some of his cocky swagger – and he displayed his fear by becoming angry.

He leaned forward in his chair, his face reddening and his eyes bulging.

'Look, you slimy little jobsworth, if you don't fucking write me that referral I'll smash your fucking head in.'

I tried to remain calm although inside I was absolutely wetting myself. I had rapidly lost control of the situation and all of a sudden there was a very real chance that I was going to get hit. A confused 90-year-old lady once took exception to my attempting to perform a blood test and tried to bite me. Fortunately for me, her complete lack of teeth helped avoid any serious injury. Other than that I had managed to avoid ever being harmed by a patient. My run of good luck looked to be coming to an end though and unfortunately Simon looked like he could be capable of causing me some considerable injury.

'Look, Simon, you've got a court case to prepare for tomorrow and the last thing you need is another assault charge hanging over you.'

I would like to think that I spoke calmly and confidently to Simon, but I probably sounded like the gibbering wreck that I truly felt.

Simon looked me up and down as if weighing up his options. Clearly giving me a good beating was one of them, but thankfully instead he opted to storm out muttering 'wanker' audibly under his breath.

A few days later I read in the local newspaper that he had been found guilty of racially aggravated assault and given a three-year prison sentence.

Removing patients from lists

According to a recent report in the press, there has been an increase in complaints about patients being unfairly removed from general practice lists. If the tabloid reporting of the situation is to be believed, these decisions are left up to heavy-handed receptionists and managers, who act like overzealous doormen and will boot you 'off the list' if you dare tut at the nurse running late or are unfortunate enough to suffer from the wrong sorts of ailment.

The reality is that, for the vast majority of practices, taking someone off their list is a rare occurrence and a last resort. I had been a GP for several years before I even knew that such a drastic measure was an option. It only crept into my consciousness when a patient suggested he was going to forcibly remove my testicles from the rest of me and then encourage me to ingest them. His language was more colourful, but you get the idea. I had refused to write him a letter that stated he was too unwell to attend his probation appointment that afternoon and it hadn't been a popular management decision. To be fair to him, he hadn't carried out his threat despite the fact that my room is frighteningly soundproof and exceptionally well equipped with scalpels and tongue depressors. I was regaling the consultation details to an amused colleague when the practice manager overheard and felt it suitable grounds to 'off list' him. I was quite surprised; after years of working in A&E and inner-city GP practices, I had become well-accustomed to receiving threats and abuse at the hands of patients and fully accepted it as just being part of the job.

The only other patient whom we have threatened to kick off our list recently is a serial non-attendee. She makes appointments and then doesn't turn up. When this had happened 10 times in an eight-month period, we explained that it wasn't fair on other patients and that wasting her appointments was increasing waiting times for everyone else. When she missed two more appointments in the following month, we threatened to take her off our list. It is the only weapon we have in our armoury to try to prevent her recurrent non-attendance, but my dilemma is that I don't really want to kick her out. She and her family have been at our surgery for years and they have a lot of problems, both social and medical. The practice and our staff are one of the few constants in her otherwise chaotic existence. I also know that by throwing her off our list, I am basically just passing one of our most difficult patients on to another of the local practices. That practice would be unlikely to thank us and could take revenge by off listing a couple of their problem patients who would in turn come to us. The tit-for-tat patient dumping could last for generations. So far we have kept her on our books, but if anyone has any good ideas for encouraging her to keep her appointments, they would be much appreciated.

Far more common than forcibly eliminating patients from practice lists is patients voluntarily removing themselves. Doctors are human and you will get on better with some than others. Often patients shop around until they find a GP or a surgery that suits them and this system seems to work well enough the majority of the time. If I ever reach the point where I am regularly removing handfuls of patients from my list due to minor complaints or disagreements, it is probably time to hang up my stethoscope and find a different job. If you as a patient have just been forcibly ejected from your sixth GP practice in as many months, it is probably time you booked onto one of those anger management classes everyone keeps telling you about.

Bravery

Standing up to mildly threatening patients who are larger and better at fighting than me is about as bold as I ever have to be at work. Whereas other emergency services have to valiantly risk their lives fighting fires or arresting dangerous villains, medics are rarely required to face great personal risk in the line of duty. However, just occasionally there is an exception.

Karla Flores was a Mexican seafood vendor who was minding her own business selling seafood at the roadside in her home state of Sinaloa. Like many parts of Mexico, turf wars between rival gangs often result in violent street battles and, unfortunately for Karla, she was inadvertently caught up in one such skirmish. After hearing an explosion, she was knocked unconscious. She awoke in hospital to discover that she had been hit by a live grenade shot from a grenade launcher. The grenade was lodged between her jaw and the roof of her mouth. It was a miracle that it hadn't exploded, but it was very much live and could go off at any time.

Were the grenade to explode, anyone within a 10-metre radius would almost certainly be killed, and so understandably the Mexican doctors weren't exactly falling over themselves to take on Karla's care. Eventually four brave medics stepped forward and agreed to operate on her. In order to avoid the very real possibility of blowing up the entire hospital, it was decided that the operation would take place in an open field some distance from any civilisation.

Two anaesthetists, a surgeon and a nurse operated on Karla in an attempt to dislodge the live grenade. The team wore no protective clothing and risked their lives during the four-hour operation. It had to be done under local anaesthetic, which meant that poor Karla was awake for every second. It was a success. Karla has a scar on her face and has lost half her teeth, but she is now alive and well. To those brave Mexican medics, I salute you. You are much, much, much braver than me!

Amazingly, Karla Flores isn't the only person who has required the surgical removal of live ammunition from her person …

Foreign bodies

... According to urban legend, an old World War Two veteran was admitted to a London hospital with a live artillery shell lodged up his rectum. He had apparently been struggling with large haemorrhoids, the worst of which would hang down and get stuck on the seam of his underpants. In order to rectify this nuisance, the resourceful old chap would use an old artillery shell he had lying around to push the haemorrhoid back up into his rectum. This technique worked well for some time until the shell got stuck and he had to hobble to the local emergency department for it to be removed. It was only when the doctor was about to stick his fingers in the gent's rectum to remove the shell that he casually mentioned that the shell was still live. Apparently the bomb squad were called and they constructed a protective lead box around his anus and then defused the shell while it was still up his bottom.

For most of us, the idea of placing any sort of foreign object up our anuses is objectionable, but it is in fact a surprisingly common A&E presentation. So much so these days that it may barely raise a snigger from your seasoned emergency medics. However, there is no getting away from the fact that everyday household items stubbornly wedged in a rectum make for fabulous X-rays. There was a time when copies of these precious X-ray films were kept hidden away in the secret drawer of the head radiologist, but with the advent of the internet, we are all now just a few clicks away from being able to enjoy their irresistible attraction. My personal favourites are:

1. A key (I'm always losing mine, but hopefully not there)
2. A torch
3. A mobile phone (apparently there were several missed calls before it was removed)
4. A jar of peanut butter
5. A handgun
6. A light bulb (like a eureka moment, but in reverse)
7. A pint glass
8. Cement (it went in as liquid, but didn't stay that way for long)
9. A perfume bottle
10. A vibrator and a pair or salad tongs (when the vibrator got stuck, rather than bother the busy A&E staff the patient decided to remove the dildo himself using a pair of salad tongs … until these got stuck too!)

Retrieving the gerbil

Before finally leaving the essential medical subject of funny bum stories, it would be a travesty not to mention the marvellous story of the two gents who ended up in the severe burns unit of a Salt Lake City hospital.

As part of their foreplay, Eric and Andrew frequently enlisted the aid of their pet gerbil Raggot. Eric inserted a cardboard tube into Andrew's anus and then slipped Raggot in. Normally Raggot would make his own exit, but on one occasion he refused to leave the relative comfort of Andrew's back passage. While peering into the tube, Eric decided to strike a match, hoping that the light might attract Raggot and lead to his departure. Unfortunately the match ignited a pocket of intestinal gas and a flame shot out of the tube setting fire to Eric's hair and severely burning his face. Raggot the gerbil was also set alight and with his whiskers and fur ablaze went on to ignite a larger pocket of gas further up the intestinal tract. The resulting explosion propelled poor Raggot out of Andrew's anus like a cannonball. As well as second-degree burns to his face, Eric suffered a broken nose from the impact of being hit directly in the face by a rocket-propelled gerbil. Andrew suffered first- and second-degree burns to his anus and lower intestinal tract. The extent of Raggot's injuries were not documented.

The chemical cosh

I hadn't known Stan before his dementia set in, but by all accounts he was a placid soul. His wife Eileen described him as a devoted husband and father who wouldn't hurt a fly. The Stan before me now was very different. Most of his time was spent passively in his chair mumbling incoherently to himself. At other times he became agitated and angry and struck out. He rarely recognised his nearest and dearest, and the previous week in his fear, frustration and confusion, he'd hit his wife Eileen with his walking stick. Eileen was devastated. She kept telling me that the real Stan would never hurt her and would be mortified if he could comprehend the consequences of his actions. Eileen's love and commitment towards her husband never ceased to amaze me – it took a lot for her to ask me for help. This particular morning she was in floods of tears as she requested something to sedate him. Her biggest fear was that unless his aggression was controlled she would end up having to put him in a nursing home, which, in her words, 'would break both of our hearts'.

I read recently that one in four patients with dementia are being prescribed antipsychotics in order to sedate them and control difficult behaviour. Some have interpreted this as carer

211

laziness, believing that carers don't want the inconvenience of actually looking after people with dementia. Eileen is often distraught and exhausted but never lazy. She is a devoted wife who wants to try to care for her loving husband who has been transformed beyond all recognition by the dementia caused by his Alzheimer's disease.

Prescribing an antipsychotic is not something I take lightly and it was not my first course of action. We had tried normal antidepressants and also non-pharmacological techniques such as keeping good lighting and getting more help in. Antipsychotics really are a final resort. They are strong drugs with potential side effects and I spent some time talking through the possible pitfalls with Eileen. We decided to start with a low dose of quetiapine. This antipsychotic is not licensed for dementia care, and may well increase the risk of him having a stroke, but with Stan, I believed it to be the right decision.

Dignity is a word that is now regularly associated with regard to caring appropriately for the elderly and some relatives have complained about antipsychotics robbing their elderly relatives of their dignity through over-sedation. Decisions on whether to prescribe the drugs or not are a delicate balancing act and each case has to be looked at individually. Antipsychotics are not used to treat people whose dementia is at an early stage. They won't be thrown down the throats of people who have misplaced their door key or forgotten a dental appointment. They are prescribed for agitated, disturbed patients during the last stages of this awful disease.

As always, when I'm making these difficult decisions, I resort to the simple question of 'What would I want if it was me?' If I was suffering with advanced dementia and striking out at my family, would I want to be chemically coshed with an antipsychotic? It might sedate me and I might even die sooner as a result, but wouldn't that be better than the painful indignity of confused aggression directed towards the people I love and who love me?

Medical science

'Dr Daniels, I've decided I want to leave my body to medical science.'

'Oh right ... okay. Is that the only reason you've come to see me today?'

Donald clearly sensed my general lack of excitement, and he looked more than a little disappointed.

'I've been thinking long and hard about this, Dr Daniels, and I want medical science to benefit from my death. A cure for cancer could be discovered thanks to experiments on this very body,' he proclaimed proudly, patting his beer belly. 'What a legacy that would be to leave for the human race.'

'Well, yes. Erm ... thanks very much for that,' I managed to muster, trying not to give away my feeling that Donald had a slightly over-inflated view of his potential value to medicine. I wasn't convinced that the corpse of a retired used-car salesman from Liverpool was necessarily going to unlock the secrets of eternal health. However, despite the slightly narcissistic nature of his offer, his heart was in the right place.

His wish made me think about the poor people who had donated their bodies to my medical school. Perhaps they too thought that their remains would offer great benefits to the world from which they had departed. Little did they know that instead they were being left mercilessly in the hands of a horde of incompetent first-year medical students. Every Thursday morning we would prod away at bits of body with very little clue as to their anatomical whereabouts, often while nursing a terrible hangover. Looking back, I wonder quite what I gained from the dissection experience. It did help desensitise me early on to the brutality of being faced with a dead body, but I always found it easier to learn my anatomy from the anatomy colouring book rather than from poking around inside real dead people. I just hope that a few of my more studious colleagues achieved greater enlightenment and inspiration from the experience.

On reflection I decided that Donald deserved more encouragement for his decision: 'I think it's really great that you are willing to donate your body to medical science, Donald. Well done you. Are you on the organ donor list too? Wouldn't it be amazing to have one of your organs live on in someone else's body and keep them alive when you are no more.'

'Yeah, I thought about that, Dr Daniels, but I've had to say no on that one.'

'Oh, why's that?'

'Well, what if my organ went on to help someone who I didn't agree with?'

'What do you mean?'

'Well, what if part of my body was given to a terrorist or a suicide bomber or something? I wouldn't want that.'

'I think a blown-up suicide bomber would probably need a little more than one of your kidneys to keep them alive, Donald.'

'Well, yeah, but you know what I mean. What I'm saying is that I would want some sort of clause on my donor card to say that my organ wouldn't go to a religious extremist or a paedophile or someone like that.'

'Isn't being an organ donor about just helping someone else regardless of who they are? It's about giving a complete stranger the gift of life. A stranger to you – but for someone else, a beloved father or daughter or wife. Through your generosity, you could extend someone else's life for potentially decades to come.'

Donald paused.

'I can sort of see what you're saying, Dr Daniels, but I just couldn't die peacefully knowing that one of my organs could live on in a Manchester United fan.'

Gastric bypass

'It's this gastric band. It's not working. Something has to be done, Doctor!'

I'd never met Donna, the woman sitting in front of me, before, but I recognised her. Every morning I pop into the local Tesco Express near my surgery to grab a sandwich for lunch. Normally this task is carried out in a foggy blur of early-morning grogginess; I rarely notice my fellow shoppers. However, today had been an exception. And now, the patient facing me in my office, I realised, had been in front of me in the check-out queue that morning. She had caught my attention because she'd bought herself an entire chocolate cheesecake for breakfast and proceeded to tuck into it even before she'd left the shop. Please don't think that I am some sort of evangelical health-food fanatic; chocolate, cheese and cake are three of my favourite things. A chocolate cheesecake is a thing of great splendour, something in which I have indulged on many occasions, but this was 7.45 on a Monday morning. Who eats a chocolate cheesecake for breakfast?

'What's been going on then?' I asked Donna.

'Well, when I eat, I always feel sick. I think there's something wrong with the gastric band. I'm not even losing weight.'

Even without a gastric band I think that eating an entire choc-olate cheesecake for breakfast would have made me feel a tad nauseous. Thanks to a bariatric operation, my patient had a band restricting her stomach to only a quarter of the normal capacity. If today's breakfast was representative, of course she was going to feel sick after meals.

'Who put the band in?'

'The NHS wouldn't do it so I had to go private, but I can't afford to go to see them again. It cost me a bloody fortune to do it in the first place. What a waste of money.'

Looking through the notes I could see that Donna had come in many times over the last few years requesting help with weight loss. A previous GP had referred her to have a gastric band fitted on the NHS, but the request had been rejected because she didn't fulfil the criteria: patients need to have spent at least two years trying to lose weight through exercise and diet programmes. Clearly not prepared to wait, Donna had found the money to get the op done privately.

I'm not against the idea of weight-loss surgery being performed on the NHS. Ideally we would all be slim and healthy due to vigorous diets and abundant exercise, but the reality is not that straightforward. Many people simply can't manage to control what they eat and so end up overweight. When the weight starts getting to dangerous levels, a gastric band can completely turn someone's life around. Some might argue that the cost of the procedure should never be fronted by the taxpayer, but successful gastric band operations can often cure expensive diseases such as diabetes and high blood pressure, returning to health and work people who were previously facing a future of illness and disability. The potential *savings* to the taxpayer are enormous.

Most patients who have a bypass operation simply can't manage big meals any more. They feel full and sick if they eat too much, and soon learn to lessen their portion sizes. But I guess Donna was finding that old habits die hard.

'Donna, I don't think you need to see a surgeon. The gastric band is doing what it's supposed to do.'

'But this band makes me feel sick all the time.'

'No, you will feel sick if you try to eat as much as you did before the operation.'

'But I never really ate much anyway and now I eat even less.'

Donna looked suitably insincere – so much so that I didn't feel I needed to mention that I had witnessed her choice of breakfast that morning.

'Let's make a deal. I want you to promise that you'll make a massive effort to eat much smaller portions of food for the next two weeks. If you can do that but find you are still feeling sick I'll refer you to the surgeons on the NHS.'

Donna nodded with what I took to be genuine earnestness, and, sure enough, she didn't return. I'm hoping that next time I see her, the nausea will have gone and along with it some of the weight.

Karen's baby

I like doing antenatal checks; it is one of the few times during my day that a patient isn't coming to see me because they are unwell. The process of measuring pregnant tummies, listening to foetal heartbeats and having chats about baby preparations is a lovely part of my job. Karen's appointments had been no exception. She was very excited about the arrival of her first child. The pregnancy had been normal and her antenatal appointments with me had been unremarkable.

I only got wind that something had gone wrong when I received a letter from the hospital. Karen's waters had broken a few weeks early, and her baby had then started to show signs of distress during the later stages of labour. The hospital team had initially tried to use forceps to get her baby out and then went on to perform an emergency caesarean section. They discovered the umbilical cord was wrapped around his neck. When he was finally delivered, the baby didn't start breathing. The paediatric team tried to resuscitate him with oxygen, and when he still didn't breathe he was put on a ventilator and rushed to the neonatal intensive care unit.

It was touch and go for several days, during which Karen barely left his cot side. Her baby son Wesley had been starved of oxygen for too long during the birth, and it had caused some damage to the brain. Ironically, by a mechanism I don't fully understand, the oxygen that was then given during the resuscitation period to keep him alive went on to cause further brain damage. The brain scans confirmed that quite extensive damage to Wesley's brain had occurred, but the neonatal specialists explained that only time would tell how severely disabled he really was.

It was several months before I met Wesley for the first time. He had been kept in the special care baby unit for 12 weeks and there were all sorts of ongoing problems. For Wesley to leave hospital he needed to have a mobile oxygen supply and also a special feeding tube that went into his stomach via his nose. I popped in to see how they were getting on on my way home one evening. 'He's gorgeous,' I said, as I peered down at Wesley in his specially modified cot. If I'm completely honest, he wasn't gorgeous. He was odd looking with a large forehead and bulging eyes. He could sometimes focus on light in the way that a baby a few days old might, but he wasn't smiling or showing the sort of interest in the world that a normal three-month-old would.

Karen looked down at her son with immense pride, and it really moved me to witness the overwhelming strength of a mother's love. From the outside all I could see was an abnormal-looking disabled baby, but the maternal bond she had with her son was as strong as any mother's could be.

As I stared down at Wesley, his eyes wandered aimlessly in different directions and I wondered just how much he would develop over the months and years to come. As a parent myself, I can't possibly imagine how it would feel to care for a severely disabled child. My fatherly love has always been quite selfish. I've always adored my children, but it wasn't until they started giving me something back that I really began to fall in love with them. The sleep deprivation and constant screaming drove me to distraction until that first precious smile melted my heart. I was completely enthralled when my children started to grab things and then roll over, sit up, crawl, babble, talk and walk. These are all just normal developmental milestones that we reach, but for me, I needed those milestones to make the purpose of parenthood tangible. Would I be able to love and care for a baby like Wesley who might never reach even the most basic stages of human development? I would like to think I could be as amazing as Karen and offer unconditional parental love, but I'm not so sure. I guess until faced with the same scenario, none of us can be completely sure how we would react.

Over the coming months Wesley remained stable. So, when he reached four months old, Karen was able to take him on outings to meet up with other mums with similarly aged children. Most normal four-month-old babies still don't do a great deal, so the contrast wasn't too marked. As the months passed, however, the difference between Wesley and the other babies became much more obvious. Though Wesley grew in size, he continued to lie passively like a newborn while his peers starting sitting up and babbling. He was also having regular seizures, which would upset the other mums. The obvious contrast between Wesley and what was considered 'normal' was becoming too much for Karen to bear. She started to withdraw herself and Wesley from the world and spent more and more time at home. She had to tell her boss that she wouldn't be able to return to her job after her maternity leave ended, because she didn't believe that anyone else would ever be able to look after Wesley and provide him with the care he needed. Her relationship with her husband also started suffering.

One day, she came to see me asking for counselling and an

antidepressant. Her love for Wesley remained as strong as ever, but the rest of her life seemed to be crumbling around her.

I spent a brief period working in obstetrics in Mozambique early in my career. Most of the babies seemed to pop out with minimal intervention needed, but, as in this country, there were times when things went wrong. I can remember one occasion when a baby boy was born like Wesley with the cord around his neck. The midwife wiped him down and gave him a few pats, but he didn't start breathing. In a slight panic I rushed over to get the oxygen. Mo, one of the local doctors, put his hand on my shoulder as if to say 'stop'. There were no ventilators or intensive care units where I was working, but there was some oxygen and a face mask. I didn't understand why Mo wouldn't let me at least give it a go.

'His brain has been starved of oxygen for too long,' Mo calmly told me. 'It wouldn't be fair to try to revive him.'

I was shocked at Mo's attitude. He had been such a caring and compassionate doctor up until now. Surely this baby deserved a chance?

I ignored his advice and took the baby over to the oxygen machine and fitted the tiny oxygen mask over his face. As I was struggling to turn on the oxygen cylinder, I could feel the baby's mother's desperate eyes watching my incompetent fumbling. Mo came over and calmly took control, expertly performing neonatal CPR on the tiny motionless little boy. We kept going for several minutes but stopped when it became clear that we were not going to save him. All the way through the resuscitation, the mother had watched us in complete silence. When we finally stopped, she started wailing. The cries were so loud you could hear the unrestrained anguish. Mo wrapped up the lifeless baby in a towel and handed it back to the grieving woman before we made a shamefully quick exit. I couldn't bear to hear that raw grief, so I walked further and further away. It was a painfully long walk before I could no longer hear her.

Over a beer later that evening, Mo tried to explain to me why he hadn't wanted to attempt resuscitation. 'These people are very poor,' he explained. 'They can't afford to have a disabled child who won't be able to look after himself. That mother needs to be able to work to feed the other children, but she wouldn't have been able to if she had a disabled child. The whole family would suffer.'

'But surely it's not for us to make a decision based on this?' I countered.

'No, it is God's job to decide and he made his decision when he put the cord around the baby boy's neck.'

Sometimes I wish that I too believed in God so that I could justify some of the terrible things I've seen as simply being a divine will.

However much pain and hardship Wesley has caused Karen, I'm 100 per cent sure that she wouldn't for a moment wish that he hadn't been resuscitated. While resuscitated babies are left with varying degrees of disability, others make full recoveries. I would like to think that we should value the lives of all these children, but I sometimes wonder if there might be a point when quality of life would appear so limited that we question the ethics of artificially maintaining life. As a doctor, I can't give an answer to when this point should be any better than anyone else. Wesley is now nearly two years old and he is still at the developmental stage of a newborn baby. Karen tells me he seems to like it if she plays him music and gently rubs his tummy. Is that a quality of life worth all the suffering? Karen would say yes. I'm not so sure.

Notes

Several reviewers of my first book suggested that the funniest part was the section on medical notes. I could be a little offended, as this was the only chapter in which I made absolutely no creative contribution. However, given its popularity, I thought I would offer a few more humorous excerpts apparently extracted from genuine medical records:

1. The patient left the hospital feeling much better, except for her original complaints.
2. Patient's fluid intake is good, mostly beer.
3. Patient has neck veins distended down to ankles.
4. I will be happy to go into her GI system; she seems ready and anxious.
5. The patient states there is a burning pain in his penis that goes to his feet.
6. Her leaking occurs with coughing, sneezing, and exercise such as running. She would like to do more exercise, but the incontinence inhibits her. She does, however, carry on water sports.
7. She has been informed that she is pregnant by her GP.

8. Kindly see four-year-old James, who has had a cough since yesterday. Also, the family pet dog has had a similar barking cough for the last few days.
9. I should be grateful if you could see Mrs Y, who has halitosis of both great toes.

Nurses I

I had just arrived for my A&E shift, and to my pleasant surprise the department looked relatively calm in comparison to a normal Friday evening. There were no trolleys in the corridor and even some of the cubicles were empty. 'Doesn't look too bad,' I remarked to Sian, one of the nurses. 'Don't jinx it,' she said. 'I really need to finish on time tonight. It's my daughter's 10th birthday and I promised her I would be home before she goes to bed. I always seem to be working on her birthday.'

The evening wore on and it was just how I like it: a constant stream of patients coming in and out but none of the frantic chaos that so often accompanies working in the emergency department. A couple of hours into my shift I was asked to see Bill, an elderly gent who was confused and agitated. Clara, his worried daughter, was trying to calm him down, but in his confusion he was just mumbling a few words and continually trying to pull off his oxygen mask. Clara had been trying to persuade her dad to see a doctor for months but he had steadfastly refused. He had been stoically ignoring a horrible-looking infected ulcer on his foot. But it had got so bad that the infection had taken hold and he was now too unwell to object to being brought to hospital by the paramedics.

Bill was dehydrated; I needed to put in a drip so that we could give him some fluid, but every time I thought I had calmed him down enough to put in the needle, he would jerk his arm away at the vital moment causing the needle to burst his vein. Searching his arms, I realised I was running out of good veins. I was going to need some help.

'Sian, could you just give me a quick hand?'

'Sorry, Ben, my shift finished 10 minutes ago and I really need to get away on time tonight.'

I quickly scanned the area, but there was no one else free.

'I just need you for two minutes. I can't get a cannula in this patient. Could you just hold his hand and keep his arm still?'

'Two minutes!' Sian repeated sternly before she reluctantly followed me into Bill's cubicle.

Ten minutes later I was still trying to find a decent vein to cannulate. Thankfully, Sian was doing a sterling job keeping Bill calm and, most importantly from my point of view, holding his arm still. She was even chatting away warmly to his daughter Clara and helping to distract her from how poorly her father was. To all of our relief, I finally got the needle into the vein and gently slid the cannula in place.

'Thank you so much, Sian. Just keep his arm still for 10 seconds longer while I find some tape to really secure this cannula – I don't want him to pull it straight out.'

Just as I began to turn round, Sian grabbed my arm. I twisted back to find Bill had suddenly slumped forward and let out a gasp. His eyes, which had previously been shut, were now open.

'BILL!' I shouted, grabbing his wrist, but there was no response and no pulse. Within a moment Sian had shouted to the ward clerk to put out a crash call and lowered the bed flat so she could start chest compressions. When the rest of the doctors came running,

Sian let someone else take over and gently shepherded Clara out of the cubicle and into the relatives' room. I stayed with Bill and we carried on doing our best to resuscitate him.

I wish Clara hadn't had to witness that first stage of CPR. However many times I'm involved with a resuscitation attempt, the brutality of chest compressions is never lost on me. The force needed almost always cracks ribs, and I would hate to witness it being carried out one of my loved ones.

The anaesthetist skilfully intubated Bill while I was still doing chest compressions. After each two-minute cycle we stopped to see if there were signs of life or a rhythm on the monitor that could respond to a shock from the defibrillator. Neither occurred and after 20 minutes it became very clear that Bill wasn't going to make it. When we agreed to stop, I knew it would be my job to break the bad news to his daughter.

As I walked into the relatives' room, Sian was sitting holding Clara's hand, a cup of tea in front of each of them. Bill's daughter was distraught when I told her the news; as she collapsed in floods of tears, Sian put an arm around her shoulders. Clara thanked us for everything we had tried to do for her dad and I went back out to write up my notes and see some more patients. It was another hour before I walked past the relatives' room again and to my surprise Sian was still in there with Clara. They were talking and I could see that they'd had at least two further cups of tea.

When my shift ended at 9 p.m., Sian was only just leaving too.

'I'm so sorry you've finished so late, Sian. If I hadn't called you in to help me with the cannula, you wouldn't be going home three hours late.'

'Clara asked me to stay. Her brother lived a long way away and was stuck in traffic coming over. She didn't want to be on her own, so I promised that I wouldn't leave her until he got here.'

'Won't your daughter be upset with you?'

'Yes, but she's used to it by now. It goes with the territory if your mum's a nurse.'

'Will you at least be able to claim some overtime?'

'Fat chance,' Sian snorted. 'The managers would just crucify me for working too many hours and breaking the health and safety rules. Clara really appreciated the time I spent with her and that's enough for me.'

Nurses II

Personally, I think nurses like Sian are among the unsung heroes of this country. An average salary for a UK nurse is around £24,000 per year, which is less money than some Premier League footballers earn in a day. Despite this, nurses are regularly demonised by the media and government alike.

In a speech given in March 2013, the then Health Secretary accused nurses of 'coasting', and stated that too much of the NHS is focused on reaching minimum targets, 'at any cost'. He suggested that NHS staff were primarily striving only to not come last, rather than achieving world class levels of excellence – the gold medals of health care. As the UK still basked in the proud glow that followed the 2012 Olympics, a comparison between athletes and nurses seems an effective way to suggest that hospital medics should strive to achieve better.

Perhaps the most obvious difference between the 2012 Olympians and NHS hospital staff is the funding the government provided for them. When the London 2012 bid was announced as successful, the government provided careful planning, support and money to our athletes, and in the summer of 2012 the results were there for all to see. The vast majority of nurses and doctors actually do start their training aspiring to achieve 'world class levels of excellence', in much the same way that an athlete might in the early stages of his or her career. For medics, though, the ability to achieve these goals is often then compromised when we are told that we need to care for more patients with less staff. We are also expected to complete increasing piles of paperwork, which keep us away from our patients.

When this causes standards of patient care to slip, we are vilified for lacking in compassion. It's the equivalent of criticising an Olympic rowing team for not winning gold even though their boat was broken and two out of four rowers had been replaced with extra coxes shouting opposing instructions. It's no surprise really that nurses and doctors are too often simply relieved to reach the finish line intact, rather than struggling on to win the gold medals that would give the Health Secretary his glory.

I do agree with the Olympian/nurse analogy on one level. You could throw as much money, coaching and facilities at me and I could never become an Olympic athlete. However hard I trained and 'strived for excellence', I would never win an 800-metre Olympic gold medal. I'm just not designed for it, in much the same way that Mo Farah might make an awful nurse. Health care is not the career for everyone; there are doctors and nurses who perform poorly not because of facilities or funding but because they are in the wrong profession. I think we need to accept this early on in the training stage of medical careers and make sure we don't let people work in the NHS who will never be able to offer patients the compassion and expertise they deserve.

Thankfully, despite these poor performers often being the headline grabbers, there are thousands of nurses with the same compassion and dedication Sian has. Her Olympic moment for me was won when she missed her daughter's 10th birthday in order to sit with a grieving relative. She won't be offered an OBE or a lucrative sponsorship deal, but in my opinion she is just as deserving of a gold medal.

Paradise

It was absolutely pouring with rain, but it was our wedding anniversary and we had promised ourselves a rare midweek night out. After we'd made a mad dash from the car to the local Indian restaurant, a waiter opened the door for us and showed us to our table. As we took off our sodden coats, we watched as the drains on the street outside overflowed and an impressive stream of surface water ran down the road. We were the only ones who had ventured out on such a wretched evening.

'Miserable out there, isn't it? Like a bloody flood,' I commented to the waiter as he came to take our drinks order.

'No, sir. This isn't a flood. I am from Bangladesh and we have real floods there. Many people die.'

'Oh, well, yes, of course. Erm … I just sort of meant it as a turn of phrase.'

As if I didn't feel humbled enough, the waiter continued, 'Every day I am thankful to live in this paradise here in the UK.'

Looking out at the dark grey empty high street with the rain bucketing down, it was hard to try to picture this as paradise. There were no golden beaches or palm trees, but I knew what the waiter meant. Simply living in the UK makes us among the luckiest people on the planet. Regardless of the constant talk of economic downturns and double-dip recessions, we still live in a time and place in which the vast majority of us have food, shelter and safety almost guaranteed. I must admit that I felt slightly taken aback by the waiter's comments, but I can understand how it might feel to listen to English people complaining about the weather as they leave unwanted food on their plates and then return to their warm dry houses.

During a short stint working in Africa, I witnessed some dreadful things, which put my life into perspective. On the day I returned home I promised myself never to take anything for granted ever again. Under no circumstances would I complain or moan or whinge, and I would absolutely never ever say 'I'm starving.' Of course, I broke my promise and I do all of those things. Sometimes it requires a little reminder like this that really I shouldn't.

At work there are days when the majority of what I see is unhappiness. In the context of the 'paradise' our waiter saw in our homeland, it does seem a little obtuse. Of course, unhappiness and depression are complicated, and just because we don't live in a war zone, or suffer famine or natural disaster, it doesn't mean that there aren't some fairly horrendous things happening within my patients' lives that cause them great distress. Some patients tell me they feel guilty for how low they feel because they know objectively how lucky they are. Depression is a disease and for some of my patients it is a matter of trying to adjust brain chemicals or using therapy to deal with past traumas. But for people like me, who sometimes just get a bit grumpy about the minor inconveniences of life, I wonder if simply watching the news and gaining a bit of perspective might be more in order.

Yes/No

Often when my patients ask me for my advice it is with the expectation that I will be able to give them a quick Yes or No answer. I frequently disappoint them; the great majority of decisions made in general practice are a shade of grey as opposed to black and white.

For example, one patient might ask me if she should take a cholesterol-lowering drug, or another might ask me whether he should have an operation on his knee. The patient hopes I'll simply say yay or nay, but in both cases I'll actually drone on endlessly about the pros and cons. I'll recite boring facts, such as risk statistics, drug side effects and surgical complications. Eventually, after imparting my wisdom, I'll turn the question back to the patient and explain that it is their body and their decision.

However, just occasionally, I do have the very satisfying opportunity to respond to an enquiry with a definitive answer.

One such question is: 'Am I going to die, Doctor?' This is one of the rare questions to which I can be 100 per cent sure of giving the correct answer: 'Yes, you are definitely going to die. We are all going to die.' I appreciate that the patient is usually asking whether they are going to die in the immediate future, but the reality is that as soon as we try adding that sort of clarity to the answer, we start moving back into that very unsatisfactory grey area again.

'Is there a bug going around, Doctor?' is perhaps the only other question I am commonly asked that I can always answer yes to. Unfortunately there is always a bug going around. It's how bugs roll. If they stopped going around they'd die out, which sounds appealing, but according to microbiologists would result in disaster. I'll take their word on that.

A less common question asked by a patient recently was whether it was okay for him to have sex with his partner via her colostomy. Now, I really don't consider myself to be particularly prudish – patients tell me about all sorts of slightly alternative sexual behaviours and I rarely raise an eyebrow. Even if I wouldn't necessarily choose to partake in all of the said activities, anything that takes place between two consenting adults in the privacy of their own home is okay with me. Not colostomy sex, though. That's a straightforward no.

David

I don't think it will be a great surprise to any of you to hear that a reasonably high number of the patients who come in to see me leave my room without receiving a definite or immediate diagnosis from me. The great advantage I have in general practice is that time is by and large on my side. The patient in front of me is usually not severely unwell. They may well be in discomfort, worried and upset, but they are very rarely just about to expire before my eyes. This means that there is a bit more time for me to work out what is causing the aching legs, funny rash or tiredness that my poor patient might be suffering from.

However, working in the emergency department, time is often at more of a premium.

When the paramedics brought in David, barely conscious and with slow breathing, I really needed to work out quite quickly what was going on. I couldn't rouse him enough for him to tell me anything, so I was left with the tricky task of trying to deduce the cause of his comatose state from hundreds of possible causes.

The best place to start was with the information that the paramedics already had at hand. They told me that David was 31 years old with no past medical history of note. He had been looking after his two-year-old daughter while his wife was working her shift as a nurse. He was absolutely fine when she left for work, but when she arrived home she found David lying unconscious on the sofa. Fortunately their daughter was unharmed and happily watching CBeebies, apparently unaware of her father's poor health.

Why had a young, previously healthy man suddenly gone into a stupor? I started trying to work through some of the more common causes. I began with diabetes, but his blood sugar was normal. There were no signs of infection and no signs of a head injury that might have knocked him unconscious. His breathing was slow, but his lungs seemed clear. I was hedging my bets that something was going on in his brain and so was sure that the CT head scan I had just ordered was going to throw up some answers. Top of my list of suspicions was that an aneurysm in his brain had popped, causing a type of stroke. We managed to get the CT scan done pretty quickly, but to my surprise it came back completely normal.

Nearly 45 minutes had now passed and I still had absolutely no idea why David was unconscious. He was stable, but although he wasn't getting any worse, he definitely wasn't waking up. His wife had managed to find someone to look after their daughter, so was at his side, looking understandably upset and worried. I felt under huge pressure to work out what was going on. What was I missing? Barry the charge nurse wandered back from his break and took a glance at David. 'Sure he's not overdosed on something?' he asked.

'He doesn't look like a drug user,' I responded.

Barry gave me a sideways look. 'Come on, Ben, you've been doing this job long enough to know that doesn't mean a thing. He's a youngish bloke, unconscious with slow breathing. We both know the most common cause of that.'

Because David didn't fit my stereotype of a drug addict, I hadn't even considered drug overdose as a possibility. Whereas, even before my other patient Kenny introduced himself as Crackhead Kenny, it wouldn't have taken a genius to suspect that he might be a user: his clothes, his hair, his tattoos and even his smell ... everything fitted the stereotype of the archetypal drug addict. David had a young daughter and a wife who was a nurse working at this very hospital. He lived in one of the nicer parts of town, and this was a Tuesday afternoon, not a Saturday night. He couldn't have been taking drugs, could he?

Barry was never one to turn down the opportunity to get one over on me. He grabbed a pen torch and shone it into David's eyes. Both pupils were tiny. Next he grabbed David's left arm and pointed out to me the needle prick mark on his forearm. We had taken blood and put in a cannula in his right arm, so the needle prick must have already been there when David arrived at hospital. Without saying a word, Barry went to the cupboard, pulled out some naloxone and injected it into David's cannula. Naloxone is an antidote to morphine and heroin. It reverses the effects almost instantly. Within a minute David was awake, pulling off his oxygen mask and asking where he was.

Barry was trying to catch my eye so that I would notice his smug smirk, but I was too preoccupied with David and his wife. Her relief at his recovery was very quickly replaced with tears of hurt and anger. As a nurse she knew the significance of his sudden improvement following the naloxone. Through her tears she kept asking him why. David only seemed to be able to answer, 'I don't know.' It turned out that he had spent a period of time injecting heroin regularly in his early 20s but had kept away from it for years. For some reason, today his previous addiction had got the better of him and he'd tried to inject himself with the quantity of heroin that he used to take as a regular user. After such a long break, his body was naive to the drug and he accidentally overdosed.

Russell Brand talks very eloquently about the power drugs have over an addict even after years of staying clean. For some people the pull of that 'high' is something that hangs over them for ever, however settled and happy their drug-free life might seem on the outside. I learned that day that I had to leave my stupid stereotypes behind. Clearly, anyone can suffer from drug addiction.

The hardest part of the day was telling them that I was going to have to contact social services. I'm sure David was a great dad, but he had taken drugs when he was responsible for looking after his young daughter. Despite David's pleas, I just couldn't ignore that. I spent a lot of time with David and his wife, and we talked about getting help and support for them both. David had beaten drugs before, and there was no reason why he couldn't again. He had so much to stay clean for.

Hospital deaths

There have been a fair few doctors and nurses over the years who haven't exactly covered our profession in glory. It's understandable that medics who have either deliberately or accidentally killed their patients make headline news. However, just occasionally, there are hospital deaths that aren't solely the fault of the medical staff.

One medical team in a hospital in South Africa started noticing that each Saturday morning a patient who occupied a certain bed on the intensive care ward would be found dead with no apparent cause. Initially it was considered a morose coincidence, but soon staff realised that there must be some reason for the patients in this specific bed to all die within a week of arrival on the ward. The doctors feared the bed was contaminated with some sort of killer bug that was infecting the patients. Appropriate investigations were undertaken, but no bug was found. Presumably because of a lack of beds, or an unwillingness to give in to superstition, the killer bed was always refilled with a new patient each week, but the mysterious deaths continued.

Until, one day, somebody took notice of the cleaning lady as she did her weekly Friday-evening deep clean. The cleaner entered the ward, unplugged the life-support system beside the bed, and plugged in her floor polisher, before spending half an hour cleaning the ward. The staff finally realised what had been happening. Over the noise of her polishing machine, no one would have heard the gasps for breath and the death rattle from the desperate inhabitant of the 'killer bed'. The cleaner would then plug back in the life-support, leaving a lovely clean floor and a dead patient. Labelled in the press as the 'South African Floor Polisher Massacre', the exact numbers of people who died still isn't known!

(Disclaimer: I have absolutely no evidence that this actually happened, but I read it on the internet so it must be true?!)

Sinbad

As soon as I had rung the doorbell my heart sank. High-pitched yapping of a small dog was followed by the scraping of paws against the front door – always a foreboding start to a home visit.

'Sinbad, shuddup! Stop that noise!' I heard, as my patient Mrs Briggs shuffled slowly up to the door and grappled clumsily with the handle.

When the front door finally opened, Sinbad didn't allow his advancing years or excessive weight to prevent him from jumping up at my legs and excitedly sniffing around my groin. Sinbad was a fat Jack Russell with a tuft of white hair on his chin that uncannily matched the sprouting white hairs on the chin of his owner.

Mrs Briggs was a kindly lady in her 70s. She was large all over, but most notable was the size of her legs. Years of fluid retention meant that her legs had steadily expanded to the size of small tree trunks. The circumference of her thighs looked barely different from that of her ankles, with only a few creases of her tightly stretched skin to suggest where her feet joined her lower legs. Her bloated feet were completely solid, and poking out were 10 spherical toes with brittle yellow toenails nestled on top. The soles of her feet were made up of a white crust of rock-hard skin with a flaky surface and some cracked scaly patches around the heel. The only footwear that she could now fit into were some old frayed slippers that had had the back cut away.

'Do you want me to lock Sinbad in the backroom, Doctor? I know not everyone's a dog lover.'

Every part of my being wanted to say 'Yes, please', but for some reason I politely agreed to allow Sinbad to accompany us. After Mrs Briggs had sat down on the sofa, Sinbad curled up contentedly at her feet and for just a short moment I felt something close to affection towards them both.

'Thank you so much for coming out and visiting me, Dr Daniels. I've got some biscuits out specially.' With that Mrs Briggs reached over and passed me a cracked china saucer holding a number of shortcake fingers. 'Do take one,' she said.

Over the years I have had all sorts of refreshments offered to me by patients during home visits – cups of milky tea and custard creams are the norm, although I have been offered more than one gin and tonic, and on one occasion an old Rastafarian gent tried very hard to persuade me to share with him the enormous spliff he was smoking. As a general rule, I always decline the food or drink (or marijuana) offered by patients, but I'm rather partial to shortbread and I hadn't yet had a chance to grab my lunch.

I took a seat in the armchair and politely nibbled on my biscuit while Mrs Briggs began to explain why she had asked me to visit. I was making my best effort to listen intently, but I couldn't help but be distracted by Sinbad. The dog had started sniffing intently around his owner's lower legs. This in itself was only slightly disturbing, but he then started enthusiastically licking the hard crust of skin on the soles of her feet. He systematically licked the entirety of each foot in turn, even endeavouring to squeeze his tongue between each of her swollen toes. After completing this,

Sinbad focused his attention on a particularly hard callus on her left heel. After softening it up with a particularly vigorous lick, he began gnawing at it as if it was a tasty bone. I couldn't quite believe what I was seeing and initially wondered if Mrs Briggs was even aware of what was happening, but as Sinbad struggled to get a good vantage point on which to clamp his teeth, she purposely manoeuvred her foot to a more accommodating angle.

Mrs Briggs was talking away, but I had very little recollection of her words. All I could focus on was the relish with which her elderly Jack Russell was feasting on her dead skin. Surely this couldn't be healthy for either dog or human? Yet, I got the impression from their mutual sense of ease that it was in fact something that they had both been enjoying for some years. After around 10 minutes, Sinbad appeared to have had his fill of foot, but, clearly on the lookout for some dessert, he jumped up on the sofa and began sniffing around the saucer of shortbread biscuits that was perched on an adjacent side table. With the same sort of concentrated deliberation he had shown his owner's feet, he licked each shortbread finger on the plate from top to bottom and then chose one that he liked the look of and began chomping away messily.

Finally taking some notice of her dog's inappropriate dining habits, Mrs Briggs shooed Sinbad away from the saucer of biscuits and then, without the merest hint of shame, held the saucer out in my direction and offered me another. It was at this point that the harsh reality hit home. I had no way of knowing if Sinbad had already given the shortbread fingers a good going over before my arrival. Even as a glass-half-full kind of guy, I still couldn't get away from the fact that it was quite likely I had just eaten a biscuit laced with dog saliva and foot scale. My gag reflex began triggering uncontrollably and God knows how, but I kept myself together and managed to leave the premises before vomiting.

John

John wasn't the easiest of patients. He rarely took my advice on anything but still enjoyed coming to see me now and again to get a few things off his chest. He drank too much and he worked too hard and his diet was pretty awful. He didn't need me to point out that his health was suffering as a result, but like so many of us he seemed trapped in his bad habits. John reluctantly took pills for his high blood pressure, gout and raised cholesterol. He always had the aim of changing his lifestyle so he wouldn't need the medicine any more, but despite gym membership fees leaving his bank account every month, he was much more likely to grab a bottle of wine and a takeaway curry after work than eat a salad and run 10 kilometres on a treadmill.

John was in his early 50s and was still bitter about the break-up of his marriage almost eight years earlier. He blamed his ex-wife and 'that bloody bastard' she ran off with, but he did admit that he had spent far too much time working on his career and too little effort working on his relationship. He had also confided in me that his marriage had never really recovered from the stillbirth of their son 20 years earlier. He always felt that he should have somehow been able to have prevented his son's death and he explained that feelings of blame ate away at him. He had always shooed away my suggestion of counselling, instead choosing to throw himself further into work and drink.

I had seen John miserable and angry many times, but today he seemed genuinely depressed. This was the first time he was questioning the point of going on; he wanted me to keep this off his record, but he had actually begun to seriously think about suicide. I was really worried about him, and wanted him to get some help, but as usual John dismissed the idea. I thought at least he would let me sign him off work for a few weeks, but no – despite all his anger and bitterness towards his career and the detriment it had caused to his life, he couldn't quite imagine living without it. He had a fierce loyalty to his job and over the years it had taken precedence over every other component of his life. You would think that, given its hold over him, John would at least be passionate and enthusiastic about his career, but when I asked him about it, he told me that as each year passed he found it increasingly hard to take any sort of joy or satisfaction from a day at work.

Normally it's me needing to hurry along a consultation due to poor time keeping, but on this occasion it was John who brought our consultation to a close. He needed to get back to work. I watched him from my window frantically rushing back to his car.

As he accelerated out of our car park, I could just picture him speeding recklessly the few miles across town, running past his secretary, turning on his computer and grabbing his stethoscope.

I hoped his first patient of the afternoon appreciated him and wasn't too disgruntled about him starting his surgery 10 minutes late.

How doctors die

Doctors are human too, and much like many of our patients, we aren't always great at looking after our physical and mental health. We live our lives in much the same way as anyone else, and although we should really have above-average skills when it comes to self-diagnosis, we will still succumb to the inevitable eventually and shuffle off this mortal coil. Interestingly though, although doctors live their lives much like everyone else, we often choose to end them differently.

We live in a time where drugs and technology allow doctors to cheat nature and keep patients alive for longer and longer. This is a fantastic achievement of modern science and every day I speak to happy, healthy people who would be dead without our medical input. This advancement does, however, have a cost. As I write this, Nelson Mandela is still alive in an intensive care unit in South Africa. The television cameras have been kept away, but any medic can imagine what sort of life someone in his situation would be living. He is likely to be asleep much of the time with most of his waking hours spent devoted to taking medications either orally or directly into his veins. The needles and blood tests will be constant, with the desperate attempts by the medics to keep his vital organs functioning. Food would be at best puréed and at worst fed through a tube. Toileting would be via a catheter and a nappy. It seems so sad that such a great man could be reduced to this.

When we doctors talk among ourselves we often promise that we won't allow our own lives to be kept artificially prolonged in such a way. When machines and medication can keep your heart beating while nearly every other bodily faculty is failing, surely it is time for doctors to stop dragging out any last semblance of existence and let nature take its course?

As medics, our constant exposure to death and dying must affect us, and perhaps force us to consider our own mortality more intently. Personally, I still fear death, but I don't dread it anywhere near as much as I fear being kept artificially alive in a state that offers constant pain and suffering. In his essay 'How Doctors Choose to Die', Ken Murray talks about his doctor friend who was found to have pancreatic cancer. Understanding the real consequences of this, his friend declined all the surgery, chemotherapy and radiotherapy that was offered, and instead chose to spend his last months dying peacefully at home with his family around him. As a doctor he had seen enough during his career to be able to make an informed choice about how he wanted his own life to end. If he hadn't been a doctor, he may well have lived a little longer, but equally suffered a whole lot more.

But if doctors routinely choose to reject life-prolonging treatments for themselves, why do they often push so hard to keep their patients artificially alive?

There was a bad joke that went around medical school: why do coffins have the lid nailed on?

Answer: to keep the oncologists out.

As doctors, it can feel like stopping treatment is an admission of failure. We do often maintain treatment for too long, and definitely need to get better at stepping back and saying enough is enough. However, although we know that letting go is in the best interests of our patient, sometimes we fear that by withholding treatment we will be criticised and accused of callous laziness.

The Liverpool Care Pathway is a system that was set up to allow patients with terminal illness to die peacefully and with dignity. However, this protocol for allowing a natural death was picked up by many parts of the media as being cruel and barbaric. Grieving relatives accused doctors of allowing their nearest and dearest to die prematurely. Scared relatives requested that their dying relatives weren't put on this so-called 'death' pathway, and as a result many people will have died after enduring more suffering than they needed to.

Despite all the uproar about the Liverpool Care Pathway, I always find it odd that its strongest critics never asked whether doctors would ever allow themselves or their loved ones to be put on it. As doctors, why aren't we asked more often what treatments we would and wouldn't give to ourselves or our own families? When I chose a boiler for my house, I asked the plumber which type he had at home. When I'm choosing dessert in a restaurant, I ask the waitress which one she likes best. There is nothing like a bit of inside knowledge when making a tough decision – and they don't get much bigger than decisions about pudding!

Doctors make mistakes and get things wrong all the time, but we're not, as large segments of society seem to feel, part of some sort of big evil conspiracy. For example, wasn't it telling that throughout the whole MMR furore, I never met a single doctor who didn't give the MMR vaccine to their own child? In the same vein, I don't know any doctors or nurses who wouldn't allow themselves to die on the Liverpool Care Pathway.

Having said all this, of course this is only my opinion. Who am I as a doctor to decide what should and shouldn't be considered good quality of life and when care should or shouldn't be held back? We doctors are accused often enough of playing God, and so in an ideal world, patients themselves would make informed choices about how they die and be in complete charge of every decision along the way. The problem is that, in reality, once we get to this late stage in life, many of us will be too ill and confused to make any coherent decisions. Relatives will be forced to make really difficult decisions; often love for a family member will mean wanting them to be around for as long as possible. I wonder if this is what is happening at the moment with Nelson Mandela? If he is still alive at the time of reading, that is. He is loved by a whole nation, and they understandably don't want to let him go.

These difficult end-of-life decisions are never easy, but as someone who has to deal with them often my only advice is to talk to your families now and tell them how you would like to die. It is a taboo subject, but it will happen to all of us eventually. I would urge you to write a living will, also known as an 'advance directive' or 'advance decision'. Don't leave it to doctors or tearful relatives – let everyone know now what you would like to happen were you to become so ill that you could no longer make decisions for yourself.

Rita

Miss Blumenthal, the elderly Holocaust survivor, died peacefully in the night. By the next afternoon, her room in the nursing home had been filled by a new patient, Rita.

While Miss Blumenthal had been a serene and model resident, Rita was causing a bit more of a stir. I could see the exasperation on Nurse Carmela's face as she answered the front door to me.

'Oh, Dr Daniels, this lady is very tricky,' Carmela warned me as I followed her through to her room.

'Oh, come on, Carmela, she's 92 years old. How much trouble can she be?'

Rita was sitting in an armchair at the window with a cigarette held loosely between two yellow nicotine-stained fingers. There were small brown cigarette burns all over her nightie, and as we walked in she nonchalantly stubbed out her cigarette on the windowsill, completely ignoring the pristine ashtray that was just a few inches away. Rita had a tiny frame and you could make out almost her entire skeleton under her taut skin. Her hair was completely white and its straggly appearance suggested that she hadn't conformed to the blue rinse perm that most of her compatriots in the nursing home proudly sported.

'We've been telling her she can't smoke in her room but she won't listen to us,' Carmela whispered to me.

Rita turned to look at us with some disdain. ''Ere, who the fuck is he?' she asked, looking me up and down with a steely gaze.

'I'm your new doctor, Rita. It's very nice to meet you,' I smiled nervously, holding out my hand.

'He can't be a doctor,' Rita replied, completely ignoring my outstretched hand.

'He looks too young to be a doctor, no Rita?' Carmela chirped.

When I first qualified, my patients would often comment that I looked far too young to be a doctor. It annoyed me back then, but at this point I was well into my 30s and ready to take any remarks on my youthful appearance as a compliment.

'What! Nah, he don't look too young to be a doctor, just too bleeding stupid! Look at that face. Grinning like a fucking chimpanzee. Which brainless bugger gave him a medical degree? No wonder the whole bleeding country's gone down the swanny.'

Slightly taken aback, I tried again with my charm offensive. 'So, Rita, how are you settling into your new home?'

'What 'ere? This fucking shit 'ole? This ain't my bloody 'ome I can tell ya. Packed me off 'ere to die they did, but 'ere I'll tell you one thing ...' Rita leaned forward and looked around as if she was about to whisper to me a great secret that no one else should hear. 'I'LL OUTLIVE THE FUCKING LOT OF YA!' she bellowed right into my ear and then let out an enormous cackle that sent her ill-fitting dentures rattling around in her mouth.

Once she'd stopped cackling, Rita decided that my audience with her had come to an end and she shooed me unceremoniously out of her room.

'Go on, bugger off, you. I'll die when I'm good and fucking ready without no meddling doctors and their dirty snake charms.'

With that, I took Rita's less than tactful social cue to leave and wondered exactly what I could write in her medical notes that could politely summarise our consultation. I was rather looking forward to being Rita's GP for some time to come, but unfortunately the nursing home manager felt she was a fire hazard and managed to move her on to a different nursing home looked after by another GP surgery. A great shame.

Neighbours

It was 8.30 on a Friday evening, and the blessed end to a long day and a tiring week. Amazingly, I found both of my children fast asleep when I got home, and the house relatively tidy. There was a can of beer in the fridge, a surprisingly good film starting on the TV, and, most importantly, we were due a delivery from my favourite Indian restaurant. With my money at the ready, I was sitting on the sofa impatiently waiting for the doorbell to ring. I could just picture being handed over the large brown paper bag weighed down by tarka dal, chicken korma, pilau rice, naan bread, and a bag of poppadoms that had been thrown in free of charge. All of which were guaranteed to elevate my Friday evening mood even further. When the doorbell rang, I sprang to the door like Usain Bolt out of the blocks in a 100-metre final.

To my overwhelming disappointment, it was not the curry delivery man ringing our bell; it was Tom who lived across the road. Tom was in his late 60s and lived alone. He seemed to spend an unfathomable amount of time pruning his front hedge and complaining about the council's management of residential parking permits. He was friendly enough, but although I like the general notion of being neighbourly, my natural instinct was to attempt to avoid him at all costs.

'Hello Ben, I've been having a few problems that I thought might interest you what with you being a doctor. You did always say to come over any time if I needed anything.'

Keen to avoid just such a scenario, I have never admitted to being a doctor to any of our neighbours, but I suspected Tom had spotted the doctor's parking permit in my car window, giving the game away. When I had said that Tom could pop over at any time, I meant to borrow the lawn mower or a cup of sugar, not to use my house as an all-hours walk-in medical centre.

'It's my bowels, see, Ben. Something dreadful they are. Shocking it is. It's just coming away from me like an erupting volcano. All yellow and the smell really is just something else.'

'Oh,' was all I could muster as a reply. Having happily lapsed into a post-work haze of relaxation, I just didn't feel capable of switching my brain back into empathic doctor mode. I should really have interrupted Tom straight away and explained the importance of firm boundaries between my work and my home and between neighbours and patients. I didn't. Instead, I stood on the doorstep in frustrated silence inwardly willing Tom to go back home. Tom was blissfully unaware of my ebbing mood and terrible lack of empathy. If he had come to see me just an hour earlier while I was still at work, I would have listened intently and offered support, reassurance and maybe even a diagnosis. But in my head I was now off duty and I just couldn't manage any level of compassion at all.

Some of you might imagine that as a doctor I am always on duty, continually seeking out the opportunity to fight disease. The truth is, I'm not. When I'm at work I'm a doctor and mostly quite a good one. When I'm not at work, I'm a dad and a husband and someone who likes watching football on a Saturday afternoon and eating a curry on a Friday night! The only exception to this rule is a true medical emergency. Then I will step in and help if I can. I have performed chest compressions on a beach and helped at the side of the road after a car accident. Any doctor would do the same. Tom didn't have a medical emergency. He had a bad case of the squits and my 'passion' and 'love' for my job definitely didn't extend to spending my Friday evening off listening to the extensive details of his bowel movements.

About 10 minutes into my doorstep consultation, the takeaway delivery man arrived and I was optimistic that this could facilitate my exit strategy. I began to start making my excuses, but before I could interrupt Tom, my wife nimbly squeezed past me, snatched the £20 note still grasped in my hand and exchanged it for the takeaway. Before I knew it she was back in the lounge tucking into her supper, while I was still left on the doorstep with Tom, grumpily listening to his woes.

Finally, after 20 minutes, enough was enough.

'Erm, Tom, I think you need to give it a couple of days to settle down and if it's no better go and see your own GP.'

With that I finally managed to close the door and return to my relaxing Friday evening. But, despite my relief at getting rid of him, I felt an instant guilt about my indifference to Tom's distress. Over the years I've been amazed at how many of my patients are cared for by neighbours. I've witnessed some amazing acts of compassion and kindness between people whose only connection is proximity of habitation. Tom was a lonely guy who had simply wanted some neighbourly support and reassurance. He assumed that as a doctor I would be only too willing to offer that.

I looked down at my curry and found that I had completely lost my appetite. Whether this was due to my sense of guilt at my startling lack of compassion or because the tarka dal on my plate struck an uncanny resemblance to Tom's description of his diarrhoea I'm not sure.

Letter to myself, 10 years ago

Dear Ben, or should I say Dr Daniels,

It's your first day as a doctor and don't you feel grown up standing in front of the mirror in your new shirt and shiny shoes. You'll be double-taking for weeks when people call you Doctor and so you should, because you look about 14 and know absolutely nothing.

Your seniors will give you a really hard time for those first few months. Sometimes for no good reason, but mostly because you keep losing stuff and forgetting to do things. You actually got quite good at passing exams and so it will be a bit of a shock when you realise that you're really not that great at being a junior doctor. It will get better and you'll get better. I promise.

Anyway, here are some pieces of advice I would like to give you for the next 10 years that might make life a little easier:

1. For a start get a bloody haircut, Ben, and shave off those ridiculous sideburns! No, you don't look like Liam Gallagher. In fact, if anything, you look considerably more glam rock than Brit pop.
2. There will be times, particularly in those first few years, when you'll lose your way a bit. Often your job will be overwhelming

and you won't feel able to cope with the uncontrollable number of demands being placed upon you. There will be many times that you genuinely don't believe that you have time to even eat or pee. Take a step back and remember why you chose medicine. You are never too busy to spend an extra five minutes with a patient reassuring them or explaining something. You'll learn that sometimes making someone a cup of tea and holding their hand is of much more therapeutic value than yet another blood test or chest X-ray.

3. After your first week at work you'll need to let off some steam. Nothing wrong with that. Have a few drinks by all means and I won't even judge you for going to that awful nightclub after the pub shuts. Just one thing though – for the love of Jesus don't try to drunkenly persuade some girl to come home with you by telling her you're a doctor and you save loads of lives. She'll say no, but far worse, you'll later discover that she is in fact your consultant's daughter. He'll see the funny side but you'll never live it down. Never.

4. Just a few days from now you'll witness a care assistant being horrible to an elderly man with dementia. She will castigate him as if he was a naughty child because in his confusion he put salt and pepper onto his pudding. You decide to say nothing as you don't want anyone thinking you're a troublemaker. That decision not to speak up will remain one of your biggest single regrets in medicine. In 10 years' time you'll still be able to see the hurt expression in that old man's face just as clearly as the day it happened. Shame on you.

5. A few years from now you'll be in a coroner's court. It will be one of the worst experiences of your life and you'll be forced to question everything you thought you believed to be right. You'll question whether medicine is for you and if all the hard work was worth it. It is worth it and you'll get through it. The experience will make you a better doctor and, no, it wasn't your fault.

6. Let's face it, being a West Ham fan hasn't been great thus far. I imagine you'll be hoping I can give you a few tales of success and glory to look forward to over the next 10 years. I can't, but deep down I think you probably knew that. In 2006 West Ham will get to the FA Cup final, but to your dismay you'll be on call that weekend. You'll beg, lie and cheat to get that weekend off. You'll end up having to swap it for a week of night shifts and miss a close friend's birthday party as a result. The cost of the ticket you bought off a tout will be more than the value of your car (no, you don't have a nice car by 2006). After 89 minutes it looked like it was actually going to be worth all the effort and money … It wasn't. You'd have been better off going to work.

7. All the heartbreak of supporting West Ham for the next 10 years will pale into insignificance in comparison with supporting England. It will be a further decade of unrelenting disappointment and underachievement and no we don't get any better at taking penalties. If you can completely ignore the next decade of World Cups and European championships your life will be simpler and less painful. Don't get too down though; we do beat the Aussies at both rugby and cricket. Yes, I know they're posh boy sports and you don't really understand the rules, but just enjoy the winning part.

8. You'll probably want to know whether you're going to save any lives because at this stage in your career you foolishly believe that's what it's all about. You become a good doctor but not because you save lots of lives. Ninety-nine per cent of the time your patients will get better or get worse regardless of what you do. The sooner you learn this, the better a doctor you'll become. But yes, you will save the odd life, most memorably up a mountain in Peru in the middle of the night. It sounds exciting but you absolutely shat yourself at the time you big Jessie.

9. Never be too proud to ask for help. It's hard admitting your own shortcomings but your colleagues and, most importantly, your patients will appreciate your honesty. Be humble, smile and listen, and you won't believe how much you'll learn during those first few months. Ten years from now there will still be plenty of things you don't know and need help with, so the sooner you learn that you don't know everything the better.

10. Oh, and one last thing, Ben – these first few years as a doctor really will expose you to the full spectrum of human emotions. There will be moments of joy, great sadness, elation and frustration. Hidden among them, there will be also occasional nuggets of absolute comedic gold. If some funny shit happens write it down. Believe it or not, in 10 years from now you'll be struggling for material for that tricky second book and those Amazon reviewers can be a harsh lot.

Further Confessions of a GP is part of the bestselling 'Confessions Series'. Also available:

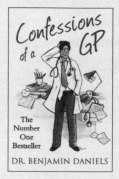

Confessions of a GP
by Dr Benjamin Daniels

Confessions of a Male Nurse
by Michael Alexander

Confessions of a New York Taxi Driver
by Eugene Salomon

Confessions of a Police Constable
by Matt Delito

Confessions of a Showbiz Reporter
by Holly Forrest

Confessions of an Undercover Cop
by Ash Cameron